Folk Stories from
the Lake District

Peter N. Walker is a successful thriller writer, as well as the author of numerous best-selling books for Robert Hale, including *Murders and Mysteries from the Yorkshire Dales* and *Murders and Mysteries from the North York Moors*. As Nicholas Rhea he has written *Portrait of the North York Moors* and the popular 'Constable' series, which was recently adapted for television as *Heartbeat*.

In 1982 he retired as an Inspector with the North Yorkshire police to concentrate on his writing. He is married with four adult children and lives in North Yorkshire.

Folk Stories from the Lake District

PETER N. WALKER

ROBERT HALE · LONDON

© *Peter N. Walker 1993*
First published in Great Britain 1993

ISBN 0 7090 5093 3

Robert Hale Limited
Clerkenwell House
Clerkenwell Green
London EC1R 0HT

The right of Peter N. Walker to be identified as
author of this work has been asserted by him
in accordance with the Copyright, Designs and
Patents Act 1988.

Photoset in Palatino by
Derek Doyle & Associates, Mold, Clwyd.
Printed in Great Britain by
St Edmundsbury Press Ltd, Bury St Edmunds, Suffolk.
Bound by WBC Bookbinders Ltd, Bridgend, Mid-Glamorgan.

Contents

Author's Preface

The English Lake District, once such a remote part of the country, is rich with folk lore. There is no doubt that many old stories have been lost or forgotten but new ones arise which may now be considered to be folk tales. Although there are different opinions as to what constitutes a folk story, I have considered those which have been re-told many times, often by word of mouth over successive generations. Inevitably, with every telling there are alterations, so in most cases where there are differing accounts, I have selected the better known version.

Examples of modern tales which might be considered as folk stories include the true story of The Beauty of Buttermere, the death of Charles Gough, the exploits of John Peel, the famous huntsman and perhaps the strange account of the spectral army on Souther Fell. There are also true stories of lost villages which now sleep at the bottom of Thirlmere and Haweswater, surely tales of the future which will be told among others like the lost town beneath Talkin Tarn.

While this collection of tales does not purport to include ghost stories, I have recounted some which may now be regarded as part of the Lake District's folk lore, such as the Calgarth Skulls, the hauntings around Thirlmere and, of course, the famous spectral army of Souther Fell.

It is hoped this modest selection of stories will add a new dimension to our love of what is surely England's most beautiful countryside.

Peter N. Walker

1   Black Combe

The Kneeling Cattle

Black Combe, alternatively known as Black Head, is an extinct volcano which is thought to be the oldest natural hill in the world. There is an easy route to the summit (said by the local people to be accessible even by those wearing carpet slippers!), and from the top there is one of the finest views in England. Four countries can be seen – England, Scotland, Wales and Ireland – and more than a dozen English counties are also visible. It is possible to identify such features as Snowdon in Wales, the Mountains of Mourne in Ireland, the Irish coastline, the Isle of Man and, on a very clear day, the Talke-o'-the-Hill in Staffordshire, more than a hundred miles away. For this extensive view, of course, a clear day is required but the summit of Black Combe is so often shrouded in mist which obscures this panorama.

The mountain rises to a height of almost 2,000 foot and overlooks the Irish Sea and Morecambe Bay; it is located on a huge piece of land which juts south into the sea over Duddon Sands across the estuary from Barrow-in-Furness. Ancient folklore tells us that in AD 540 St Patrick was shipwrecked on Duddon Sands from where he walked to a village which was named in his honour. That village is Patterdale near Ullswater where he is patron of the village church (see Ullswater).

In the village of Whitbeck upon the A595, which lies in the shadow of Black Combe, there sleeps the Lady of Annaside, a girl who died around 1300. She lies in the church dressed in her wimple and long flowing gown. She is thought to be a member of the Huddleston family who lived nearby long ago. Annaside is also the name of a hamlet on the coast, but nearby, again on the A595, is another old village called Bootle which should not be confused with Bootle on Merseyside. In the ancient red sandstone church of St Michael and All Angels are shields of the Huddlestons. The churchyard contains a miniature sundial on top of a tall metal pedestal which in turn stands upon the stepped remains of a stone cross. Inside, there is a remarkable red sandstone font with an elaborately carved oak cover.

To the north of Black Combe is Lakeland's Eskdale but in the tiny communities which surround the mountain, there is said to occur a curious event at Christmas. According to local folklore, at the stroke of midnight on Christmas Eve, the cattle kneel to adore the newborn Christ while the bees in their hives begin to sing.

There are people who claim to have heard the singing of the bees and to have witnessed the worshipful bending of the knees of the cattle at this magical hour.

2 Borrowdale

The Battle of Borrowdale

Early travellers considered Borrowdale to be a sombre and somewhat frightening place. For example, the writer, Thomas Gray, stopped at Grange near the entrance to the dale and refused to go any further. He discovered that three years prior to his visit in 1796, a large number of rocks had fallen from the overhanging crags and had blocked access to the deeper parts of Borrowdale. He might also have been influenced by a popular myth which said that if you journeyed deep into this part of the Lake District, you had to talk in whispers because loud talk or other noises could create avalanches of rocks.

For a long time, Borrowdale was regarded as a very grim place and one of its modern names, The Jaws of Borrowdale, is a reminder of that forbidding reputation. Remote and at one time almost inaccessible, Borrowdale now epitomizes the beauty and charm of the Lake District because it remains largely unspoilt. Indeed, it is considered one of the most beautiful places in England. As I toured the dale in October, cascades of water were roaring from the fells and I saw a black horse posing for a tourist's camera, while ahead the road seemed to disappear among the mountains. But I knew there was a route over the fells to Buttermere and did not experience Gray's fears. Instead, I admired Borrowdale's remote beauty.

Borrowdale lies south of Derwent Water, surely England's most attractive lake, and contains five tiny hamlets. One of them, Seathwaite, is the wettest place in

England, boasting some 140 inches of rainfall each year. Seathwaite is at the head of Borrowdale and is regularly packed with cars belonging to mountaineering visitors; the other villages are Seatoller, Rosthwaite, Stonethwaite and Grange, the latter being a modern mecca for tourists. Grange was once the site of a grange belonging to the monks of Furness Abbey, and today the village has a fine twin-arched bridge which spans the clear waters of the River Derwent. The village has shops and cafés and from nearby there are stunning views over Derwent Water and between the mountains towards Keswick.

One local attraction is Lodore Falls. It is possible to climb the falls via a footpath which begins near the Lodore Swiss Hotel on the road to Keswick. When the water is cascading over the rocks after heavy rain, it provides an enthralling experience. The water starts its downward journey in Watendlath Tarn (see Watendlath) and the poet, Robert Southey, wrote about Lodore Falls in *The Cataract of Lodore*. Another object of popular interest is the Bowder Stone. This is the largest boulder in the Lake District and stands close to the road about halfway between Grange and Rosthwaite. It is a relic of the Ice Age and rests on one point which is so slender that two people lying beneath it can touch one another from opposite sides. A ladder eases the climb to the top of this rock.

Much of the property in Borrowdale belongs to the National Trust and deeper parts of the dale are overlooked by spectacular mountains such as Glaramara and the famous peaks of Scafell, Scafell Pike, Great End, Bow Fell and Great Gable.

Tarns dot the surrounding fells, steep and winding footpaths cross them and one of England's most dramatic roads, Honister Pass, climbs from Seatoller through the mountains towards Buttermere.

In spite of its isolation, Borrowdale has seen some industrial activity. It is an area of old slate quarries and mines, and evidence can be seen in the cottages which are constructed from grey slate slabs with yet more slate upon their roofs. Many walls around the fields or upon the fells are also built of slate but another mining success came from the discovery of graphite, locally known as wadd or black lead.

The story of Borrowdale's graphite mining began, so the story says, when an ash tree was blown down during a gale. The local people discovered some strange black material among the roots and found it very useful for marking their sheep. This was graphite and as its commercial value became known over the following centuries, so Borrowdale found itself in the midst of a minor industrial boom. By the eighteenth century, commercial graphite mining was underway as entrepeneurs invaded the area and began their mining activities. Some local people felt they had been tricked into letting others benefit from the deposits and so they began to smuggle wadd out of Borrowdale.

They took it to Keswick and the coastal ports. Part of their deception was to pretend they were simpletons so that the mining masters would never suspect they had knowledge of the true value of wadd. This led to local inhabitants being known as Borrowdale gowks, gowk being the name for an idiot or fool. The truth was, of course, that these men were extremely cunning and had found ways of extracting wadd even from piles of waste; they sold it and so the local people were able to benefit from these precious black deposits.

The Borrowdale graphite was the purest known throughout the world and the famous mine, shown on some maps as the Plumbago Mine, was on the lower slopes of Grey Knotts, slightly to the north-east of where Sour Milk Gill enters the River Derwent at Seathwaite. It is now disused. Its extraction was commercialized locally for the manufacture of lead pencils at Keswick. These were the world's first lead pencils and pencil manufacture continues to be a lakeland industry sited in Keswick. At the pencil factory, there is a fascinating pencil museum which is open to the public.

The manufacture of lead pencils began at the time of Queen Elizabeth I and it did not take long for the purity of Borrowdale graphite to be appreciated. George II passed an Act of Parliament to protect it and it was his restriction which led to the smuggling of graphite from Borrowdale. There are tale of fights, murders and smuggling on the fells.

Additonally, graphite was used in the manufacture of ammunition such as cannon balls, shells and round shot. It was also used in the dyeing industry and was utilized to stop iron from rusting thus it was considered extremely valuable. The dales people even reckoned it could be used as a form of medicinal cure; after being beaten into a powder, a tiny amount, 'as much as could be placed on a sixpence' was mixed with white wine or ale and used as a cure for stomach ailments.

Such was the demand for graphite that thieves entered the mine in secret to steal it, consequently armed guards became necessary; the miners themselves were stripped and searched as they left work in case they were smuggling small rods of the precious wadd. And when it was being officially conveyed from the mine, all transport was guarded by armed men.

The mining of Borrowdale graphite ended around the turn of the century and, today, inferior graphite which is cheaper to obtain and process, comes into the Keswick factory from other countries. As a result, Borrowdale wadd is no longer mined but stories of those days remain.

One tale involves Black Sal, a woman who lived at Rosthwaite. She was one of the most successful wadd smugglers but the legend says she was hunted by wolf hounds and killed on Thornythwaite Fell which towers above Seathwaite. Years later, when flood waters demolished the front wall of the cottage in which she had lived, a piece of wadd was discovered in the wall, having been concealed there, probably by Black Sal.

Another story concerns a footpath called Moses Trod, named after one of the smugglers' ringleaders. After obtaining the wadd, Moses would lead the thieves to Keswick at night by the light of lanterns. There they would dispose of their graphite.

During their searches around the mine, dozens of lights could be seen bobbing around the waste heaps or across the fells, but the moment the alarm sounded, every light would vanish. The entire area was left in total darkness and it was tactics of this kind which meant none of the officials could ever catch a wadd smuggler.

For all the fighting between smugglers and officials, or

between the greedy miners themselves, it is another battle which lingers in the folk memory of Borrowdale. It was a struggle between some raiding Scotsmen and the brave men of Borrowdale.

The battleground was close to where modern slate quarries have scarred the summit of Honister Pass. The confrontation took place on lower ground between Honister Crag and Yew Crag which today overlook the pass from either side of the road, the B5289. The precise date is uncertain but the contest occurred during the time of the freebooters. These were piratical raiders who invaded England from Scotland; some even raided their own people to steal and plunder. These raids occurred regularly between the eleventh and fifteenth centuries, and the term *freebooter* comes from free booty – literally, they took what they wanted without paying for it.

They were pirates on land and they stole anything of value, although cattle were especially prized. Along the borders between England and Scotland, there were many battles against freebooters. As the gangs of raiders assembled, so the defenders mustered their own people who were armed almost like miniature armies. These gangs of defenders were known as Borderers. One such gang operated from Borrowdale and were therefore known as the Borrowdale Borderers.

One night, the Borrowdale Borderers received information that a band of Scottish freebooters comprising a clan known as the Graemes were intent on raiding Borrowdale. By the time the news filtered through, the Graemes had in fact succeeded in secretly entering the dale by little-known routes and had managed to steal lots of cattle. In the time it took for the Borrowdale Borderers to react, the Graemes were already leaving via Honister Pass for the return journey to Scotland.

News of the Graemes' infiltration had been conveyed to the Borrowdale leader by scouts of the mountains, and the men of Borrowdale were shocked that the marauders had breached their defences. It was even more unsettling that they had, by cunning and stealth, managed to evade Borrowdale's guards, the dale always being considered impregnable. Recrimination would come later but there was immediate action to be taken because even now, the raiders were driving the cattle before them on their long journey back to Scotland.

Halting them would not be easy because, for security reasons, the Graemes had split their group in two. The first party was to drive the cattle across the border while the second would march behind as rearguard protection. In charge of the overall operation was a younger member of the Graeme family; his father, the clan leader, was also present but his fighting days were over and his purpose was merely to rally his members. He did so by telling stirring tales of his past achievements for the old man had never lost his spirit of adventure.

It took a considerable time for the Borrowdale Borderers to muster their men and it was during this delay that the Graemes and their booty had climbed towards Honister from Seatoller. The Borrowdale men, however, had fast and sturdy mountain ponies called prickers, and so they mounted these and gave chase. Very soon, news reached the younger Graeme that the Borrowdale Borderers were in rapid pursuit; knowing he could not outdistance them, he decided to lay an ambush on the narrow track between Honister Crag and Yew Crag, about 1,000 foot above sea level.

Some of his men would climb to the top of the lofty crags to shower rocks and fire muskets upon the Borrowdale men as they passed below. It seemed a simple operation. Behind the Scots lay the descent to freedom through Gatesgarthdale to Buttermere and there is little doubt that young Graeme thought victory would be easy.

With his men in position high on the crags above and concealed among rocks along the route, Graeme awaited the arrival of the Englishmen. As the Borrowdale leader came into view, crossing the area now occupied by a youth hostel and a slate mine, Graeme leapt into his path with his sword and gun at the ready. He was going to personally kill the Borrowdale leader, a sign of his manhood and he would use his musket, a new invention at that time. His first shot was accurate; it killed the Borrowdale leader and knocked him from his white horse but instead of retreating, the Borrowdale men galloped their tough little ponies into the mountains, surging among the rocks and scrambling on to the crags to get deep among the enemy. It was a clever move which unsettled the Scots; it was especially clever because it was done without the benefit of a leader and just below the summit there followed a fierce battle. The outcome was astonishing because the Borrowdale Borderers overwhelmed the Scots and as they fled towards Buttermere, the Englishmen swept to a stunning victory.

Among the dead was the young Graeme. His old father, however, at this point well into his seventies, survived to tell the story, but having recovered their cattle, the Borrowdale Borderers had no wish to inflict further unnecessary death. They turned around and drove their livestock back into Borrowdale, leaving the battered and beaten Scots freebooters to make their sorry way back to Scotland. When the Borrowdale men had gone, the old Graeme wept over the body of his son.

His life blood was running into a tiny stream which fed the waters of Gatesgarthdale Beck – those same waters eventually entered Buttermere Lake. Graeme senior decided that his son's body would remain at the scene of his death so it was placed within a deep cleft in the side of Honister crag. Every surviving clansman brought a piece of rock to place over the entrance. This formed a lasting memorial to their fallen leader and hero, and when the funeral cairn was complete, young Graeme's sword, shield and bonnet were placed on top. Since that time, falling rocks and tumbling screes have obliterated any sign of that memorial and danger signs now warn against venturing to the foot of this sinister crag.

Thus ended the Battle of Borrowdale but today, if you climb the mountains around Buttermere (see Buttermere), you'll see that part of the lake's water is still coloured a dark and mysterious red.

3   Brampton

The Bottomless Tarn of Talkin

Brampton, a small market town with a population of around four thousand, is on the northern boundary of the Lake District. Less than a mile inside Hadrian's Wall, it is some seven miles east of Carlisle on the A69 which leads to Haltwhistle and Newcastle upon Tyne. It should not be confused with a smaller Brampton near Appleby.

Brampton's proximity to Hadrian's Wall suggests a history stretching from Roman times and this is the case. It has been claimed that the stones from which Hadrian built his wall were quarried near Brampton and in support of this there is, about half an hour's walk from Brampton among trees beside the River Gelt, a rock known as Written Rock. It stands in an almost inaccessible position some fifty feet above the river on the north bank and bears an inscription thought to have been carved by a Roman soldier during the third century. Today, it is almost illegible but when Alfred Lord Tennyson paid a visit just over a century ago, the lettering was:

VEX-LLEG-II AVG-ON-AP-APRO-E
MAXIMO CONSULIBUS SUB AGRICOLA OP-
OFICINA MERCATI

Brampton's sense of history is revealed in its show of statues and monuments.

The popular seventh Earl of Carlisle, who was Irish Secretary in the government of Lord Melbourne, is honoured by a bronze statue on Brampton Mote, a small hill on the north-east of the town. This was once the site of a motte, a medieval castle complete with defensive ditch while a short distance to the south-east is a simple pillar known as the Capon Tree. This commemorates several followers of The Young Pretender to the throne, Charles Edward Stuart (1720-88), more popularly known as Bonnie Prince Charlie. He made his headquarters at Brampton as he awaited an attack by the Royalist forces from Newcastle. Later, on 21 October 1746, his supporters were hanged from a tree which grew on the site of that memorial pillar; it was known as the Capon Tree. They included Captain Patrick Lindsay, captain James Innes and others of lower rank. The prince stayed at a house in High Cross Street, just off the market square in Brampton and this is where he received the keys of Carlisle in November 1745.

There is another monument near the crossroads, a marble pedestal bearing a portrait in bronze of George Johnson. He was a local character who died in 1896 at the age of eighty having patiently worked on behalf of his fellows for most of his long life.

There are further monuments in the church, including one to the town's soldiers who fell during two world wars.

The parish church of St Martin is fairly modern, being completed in 1878, but it is a very splendid building constructed from red sandstone with a tower bearing a red-faced clock. It occupies the site of a former hospital chapel or almshouse. The earlier church was about a mile out of Brampton towards the west and was constructed by the Normans, probably from stones used to build the Roman wall centuries earlier.

Brampton is a small market town established around the market square. The Moot Hall dates from 1817 and its octagonal shape, surmounted by a clock, dominates the cobbled market square and town centre. It stands on the site of an older building and years ago was used as a market for livestock such as poultry and geese, along with farm produce like eggs and butter. Two flights of stone stairs lead up the outside of the building to the upper portion while below there used to be a set of ancient stocks.

Some three miles to the east of Brampton is Lanercost

Priory, and access is via a minor road. This beautiful ruin now stands peacefully on the banks of the River Irthing having once had a somewhat violent existence.

Founded in 1166 by the Augustinian Canons, it was built on the site of a former pagan temple, some of their altars being discovered in the undercroft. Lanercost priory was regularly attacked by the invading Scots and raids upon it are recorded in 1296, 1297 and again in 1346. On the latter occasion, the building was ransacked.

The monks did not give up, however, and the priory continued in its role as a great church until the reformation. In 1536, the priory was dissolved and the building looted for its stone. The red sandstone was valuable and is thought to have come from Hadrian's Wall which followed a nearby route just to the north.

In spite of its tribulations, the north aisle of this ancient church did survive for a time and until the eighteenth century was used as an Anglican parish church.

In the folklore of the Lake District, however, Brampton is known for its bottomless tarn. This is a beautiful small lake extending to some sixty acres which is rich with waterfowl. Some two miles south of the town beside the B6413 which leads via Kirkoswald and Edenhall to Penrith, the tarn is called Talkin Tarn and stands in beautiful wooded parkland of 183 acres. We arrived in the autumn when the colourful trees were reflected in the smooth surface of the tarn to provide a beautiful view from the road to Brampton.

In 1972, the lake and its surrounds were designated a Country Park and is now popular as a venue for water sports, sailing, nature study and walking.

The name of the tarn comes from the tiny village of Talkin which is nearby and it was probably formed during the Ice Age; the water is very cold and comes from underground springs. One local legend says the tarn is bottomless (although the deepest part is only 42 foot deep) while another story contradicts this by suggesting that the earlier town of Brampton lies at the bottom.

In the latter case, there is a folk tale to explain it. The story is remarkably similar to the legend of Semerwater in the Yorkshire Dales and it tells of former times when the old town of Brampton was full of rich people who enjoyed a very splendid lifestyle.

The trouble was that they were all greedy, cruel and very selfish. None would share their wealth with those less fortunate and so Brampton became known as an uncaring place. One hot and humid summer day, a ragged old beggar arrived. He was looking for food and shelter and had heard from his friends and contacts, that the people of the Lake District were kind-hearted and friendly. He had been told they would make him most welcome. He did not realize, however, that the people of Brampton were different.

He was quickly to discover the truth because when he began to knock on doors to ask for food, and to stop people in the street to seek humble shelter for the night, he was attacked, kicked, beaten, cursed and threatened with dogs. Not one of the residents offered to help him. No one would give him as little as a slice of bread or even a drink of water. Instead they chased him away with sticks and stones. After trudging through the alien streets, he found himself leaving the old Brampton battered, bruised and bewildered. He was still hungry and thirsty, and had no bed for the night. As he was leaving the town, however, a poor widow who lived in a tiny cottage on a hill, chanced to see him. Recognizing his awful plight and the condition of his clothes, she took pity on him and invited him into her home for something to eat. She had very little food, but said she was willing to share it with him.

This was the first act of kindness he had experienced in Brampton and as he enjoyed the meal and hospitality, he then revealed that he was not, in fact, a poor wandering beggar. He had been sent by God to test the generosity of the people who had become rich through God's help. Now, he would teach the greedy, uncaring people of Brampton a lesson they would never forget. When he left the widow's humble cottage, he knelt on the ground and spoke to God.

Later, as the 'beggar' wandered off towards Carlisle, a terrible thunderstorm broke out. The sky became as dark as night and the torrential rain soon became a deluge.

The earth shook and water flooded from the hills and fields. Then the old town of Brampton sank into an enormous chasm created by the earthquake and roaring waters poured into it. By morning, nothing remained except a newly formed lake. The old town of Brampton with its greedy people had vanished for ever beneath the waters of the new lake. Not a trace of it remained – except for one small cottage. Standing on the shore was the house of the kindly widow. She was the sole survivor of that terrible night but her cottage is no longer there.

Even now, it is said that if you take a boat onto Talkin Tarn and row into the very centre, you can peer into the depths and see the remains of the old town deep below the surface. Today, of course, the people of Brampton are far more welcoming to strangers!

Talkin Tarn is not alone with its tales of greed. Apart from Semerwater in Yorkshire to which I have already referred, there is another tarn at the southern tip of the Lake District which boasts a similar tale. It is Urswick Tarn which is midway between Ulverston and Barrow-in-Furness. Of it, an old poem says,

The peasants tell that years ago,
In the time of the vengeful Dane,
That a village stood where the watery flood,
Now covers o'er the plain.

Another folk tale of the Brampton-Talkin area concerns a witch known as Lizzie o' Branton. She lived in a remote cottage between Brampton and Talkin and was a peculiar old woman who dressed in oddments and bizarre clothes. She talked to wild birds and animals and had a reputation for being able to cure human ailments with herbs and magic potions. Some of the farmers believed she could influence the weather and in return for free food, she would cast spells to produce weather suitable for haytime, harvest, planting or whatever activity was currently in hand. One of her specialities was to bring rain when it was needed.

When she died aged eighty-eight in 1817, it is said that the heavens opened with an almighty deluge and the downpour almost flooded her funeral service. It was the heaviest rain that had fallen on Brampton since the legendary formation of Talkin Tarn and it was accompanied by severe gales and terrifying darkness, even though it was midday. The superstitious people of the time thought it was going to produce a repetition of that other awful day centuries earlier, but in fact it did not. When the downpour came to an end, Lizzie, the rain-bringing witch, was safely put to rest and the town of Brampton survived.

But Lizzie is not forgotten. Even into this century, naughty children were threatened with, 'If you don't behave yourself, Lizzie o' Branton will get you!'

4 Brougham

A Skull and the Shepherd Lord

Brougham, a mile or so to the south-east of Penrith among narrow lanes, is close to two main road intersections and to the merging of two rivers. Here, the A66 cross-Pennine route meets the A6 north-south route, while a short distance to the west the M6 meets some of the local main roads. The River Lowther enters the River Eamont nearby and the main London to Glasgow railway also sweeps past before it enters Penrith.

Established on such a confluence of highways, Brougham would appear to be a place of some importance – and so it was in bygone times. All the modern roads follow ancient routes, some dating to Roman times, for the Romans recognized the strategic value of this site by building a fort here. It was called Brocavum and housed over a thousand soldiers. Later, the Saxons used the premises and built a church but very little survives because the site was excavated to provide the stone for a nearby Norman castle. Today, the huge open area, which includes Brougham Moor and the hamlet of Brougham as well as the parkland, contains two ruined buildings of considerable interest. One is the former Brougham Hall and the other is the ruined red sandstone castle high above the river. Each has played it part in matters of national importance.

Henry II managed to secure Brougham from the Scots and the twelfth-century castle was built by a man called Gospatrick. Eventually, the castle was acquired by the Vipont family and passed by marriage to the Cliffords, a powerful landowning family. They possessed huge tracts of land in the north of England, especially in Cumbria and Yorkshire and were involved in some of our major historic events. One of them was among the founders of the Order of the Garter, another had the task of informing Elizabeth I that the Spanish Armada had been beaten and others took part in many of our famous victories (see also Threlkeld).

The Clifford's expanded the castle; additions included the great chamber, a great hall, the chapel and servants' quarters. By the seventeenth century, the most famous of the Cliffords, Lady Anne, was head of the dynasty and in 1660 she started to restore most of her family's neglected properties. When she died, her successors allowed the castle to fall into ruin, even stripping it of lead and wood. On its riverside site, it is a sad relic of its former glory but it is open to the public.

Another reminder of Lady Anne is the Countess Pillar which is about half a mile to the east of the castle. It stands beside the busy A66 and is easily seen from passing traffic. In 1654, Lady Anne erected this fourteen foot high pillar to the memory of her mother; it is decorated with the brightly coloured family arms and sundials.

In 1649, Lady Anne, a devout Catholic, renovated the fourteenth-century chapel which overlooks the river. Generations of Broughams are at rest in this low, red sandstone church which is close to the entrance to Brougham Hall and, between 1726 and 1934, it was the private chapel of the Brougham family.

When alterations were made in the middle of the last century, two amazing graves were found in the chancel. One was that of Udard de Brougham who fought in the crusades and whose sword was displayed in Brougham Hall. The other was a man called Gilbert Brougham. He was over six foot tall, a giant of those times. Various treasures were found in those old family graves, such as part of a charm brought from the Holy Land and an armlet or ring from the rim of a drinking vessel. These were returned to the graves and now lie buried within this old church. There are further objects of interest including a pre-Reformation font where the family's children were baptised and some beautiful oak carving as well as a fine pulpit and elegant screen. A beautiful triptych carved about 1500 was so highly regarded that it was removed in 1968 and is now in Carlisle Cathedral. The art work in the church reflects the Catholicism of the Cliffords with scenes from the Bible including the crucifixion and the descent from the cross.

Brougham Hall has also had a chequered history and is presently undergoing a massive six-year restoration scheme after which it will house museums and craft workshops.

Although it was renovated about 150 years ago, it retains its historic appearance. With a superb medieval gate, it boasted a Tudor building and a great hall which was forty foot long and twenty foot wide in which there was a sanctus bell dating from Saxon times. The famous sword of Udard Brougham which remained buried at his side from the time of the crusades until 1846 was also here. The former mansion contained a superb armoury, some of which is now in the Tower of London, and a full-size copy of the Bayeaux Tapestry.

More modern buildings included a carriage house, for it was in the 1840s that Lord Brougham invented a horse-drawn carriage which bore his name. In 1899, one of these Broughams, laden with batteries, established a world land speed record of 60 mph. The decline of Brougham Hall began in 1934 when it was bought by Major Carleton-Cowper upon the then owner, the fourth Lord Brougham, becoming bankrupt. But Carleton-Cowper hated the Broughams and openly said he wanted to see trees growing in the dining room of their home, so he sold the fixtures and fittings and ordered the demolition of Brougham Hall. During this destruction, a 17-year-old labourer was killed when some masonry fell on him, and the work ceased.

But the once-splendid Hall was now declining into a sad ruin. Later, an air raid shelter was built in the grounds because, during the second World War, officers of the Royal Tank Corps and REME were billeted here.

In 1939, Brougham Hall, along with nearby Lowther Castle and Greystoke Castle, was involved in the development of a top secret CDL tank. It could produce a thirteen million candlepower light which would blind the enemy. This was one of the most secret of World War II developments, and the work was visited by a range of VIPs, including Winston Churchill, General Eisenhower, Lord Mountbatten, General Alanbrook and King George VI. Earlier visitors to the Hall had included Gladstone, Curzon, King Edward VII and King George V.

Today, Brougham Hall is a splendid ruin, but since 1985 work has been going ahead in a brave attempt to restore this magnificent old hall.

With such a long history, it is not surprising that Brougham is the source of folk stories and in fact it boasts two enduring tales. One concerns the Brougham skull. Like stories of the Threlkeld and Calgarth skulls, this one concerns a human skull which was retained within the house. For centuries, the skull was kept in Brougham Hall, occasionally being moved from room to room when the occupants objected to its presence. One family hated it so much that they threw it outside on to a heap of manure, but from that time forward, the hall suffered the most awful torments, disturbances and hauntings. Night-time was particularly horrific with ghostly noises and screams, and so the skull was brought back into the house. Everything then settled down; peace returned to Brougham Hall.

Successive occupiers did not believe the stories and many of them tried to get rid of the skull. One family even threw it into a lake, but had to retrieve it when the hauntings made life intolerable. When the skull was in the house, therefore, everyone could live in peace and tranquillity, but whenever it was removed, the screams, hauntings, noises and terror resumed. When the skull was indoors, however, it made the resident family feel uneasy and there is no doubt it was something of an embarrassment when guests were invited. A grinning skull sitting on a window ledge, shelf or sideboard is not the most appealing of ornaments.

No one seemed to know how to deal with the matter until an anonymous member of one family decided to brick it up in one of the walls of the Hall. The skull would be out of sight, but it would remain within the house. And so the deed was done. A thick wall was hollowed out and the skull was placed inside. It was firmly cemented in position and from that time there has been peace in Brougham Hall.

The most enduring, fascinating and romantic tale involving the Cliffords, however, is that which has become known as The Shepherd Lord. As the tale is also associated with the Yorkshire Dales, it is included in my *Folk Stories from the Yorkshire Dales* but because it has such strong links with the Lake District, I repeat it here.

The story begins with the Battle of Towton near Tadcaster in North Yorkshire. This awful conflict, during the Wars of the Roses, took place in a blinding snowstorm on Palm Sunday 1461 when more than 36,000 men died in battle. It was the bloodiest battle ever fought on English soil and the waters of the nearby stream ran red with blood for three days afterwards. One of the dead was the ninth Lord Clifford, aged only twenty-six, who supported the Lancastrian cause. It was some time before the sad news reached his young widow. This Lady Clifford lived at Skipton Castle in the Yorkshire Dales and had three small children.

She knew it would not be long before the revengeful Yorkists came to dispose of her vast estates and murder her husband's young heirs. She knew she must hide her young family until their lives were no longer at risk. She sent the youngest, Elizabeth, to live with a member of her domestic household as the maid's own child and dispatched her second son, Richard, overseas to Flanders. Her biggest concern was for her eldest son, Henry, who was seven years old. He was the rightful heir to the vast Clifford estates and he, above all, must be safeguarded. After giving the matter much thought, she decided to seek the advice of one of her most trusted friends. He was Sir Lancelot Threlkeld who lived at Threlkeld Hall near Keswick (see Threlkeld).

Sir Lancelot employed a faithful shepherd whose wife was a homely, trustworthy woman. They were a loving couple who had been unable to have children of their own and would dearly have loved a family. They worked on the fells near Threlkeld, on land owned by Sir Lancelot, and when Lady Clifford considered Sir Lancelot's suggestion, an approach was made to the couple. In spite of the risks if they were caught sheltering the child, they agreed without hesitation. They would rear the young Henry Clifford as their own son. Later, Lady Clifford married Sir Lancelot and, in the meantime, young Henry lived the rough, humble life of a fell shepherd.

His foster parents had no money; indeed, if Henry had been well dressed or if he had shown any wealth in his demeanour, the local people would have been suspicious and so, although he was accompanied by a faithful old nurse, he went about barefoot in summer and spent most of his time in old, ragged clothes. He slept on a bed of straw in an outbuilding and ate the same simple meals as his foster parents. His old nurse adapted to the new routine, but when she died Henry was left alone with the shepherd and his wife. Wisely, neither Sir Lancelot nor Lady Clifford interfered with his upbringing and very soon, the boy forget his earlier life. He matured into a sensible, wise young man with a love of the outdoor life. He became an expert on wild creatures and plants, and could survive on the fells in the worst of weather. Although he was intelligent and pleasant, he never learned to read or write; his tastes were simple and unrefined and his friends were the children of the surrounding fells and villages. None learned his true identity and he remained at Threlkeld throughout his maturing years.

He was there from the age of seven until he was around thirty or thirty-one, some twenty-four years in all. From a safe distance, Lady Clifford, now Lady Threlkeld, kept a close eye on her son and she never lost her belief that he would one day resume his position as rightful heir to the Clifford estates. The opportunity came in 1485 with the Battle of Bosworth. This was the last of the Wars of the Roses when Richard III was defeated by Henry of Richmond who later became Henry VII. With this victory, the fortunes of the Cliffords were restored. Now a mature man, Henry Clifford was informed of his true identity and all former exiles were allowed to return to a normal life – and Henry was one of them.

The House of Lords in London then summoned Henry, Lord Clifford, to appear before them to take back the lands and titles that were rightfully his. Members of the House of Lords were assembled in their finery – fur trimmed robes in velvet and silk adorned with fine jewellery and diamond encrusted swords. There was a tangible air of expectancy as they awaited the mighty Lord Clifford, one of the nation's most noted landowners, a man who had escaped the wrath of others and who had survived in hiding for almost quarter of a century.

But into the chamber there ambled a labourer, a man of thirty or so who was stooped with hard work, who was dressed in the rough clothing of a rustic fellow and whose hands were thick and heavy due to years of manual work.

He trudged down the aisles with the walk of a countryman rather than the upright stance of a man of quality, and he admitted to the assembly that he could neither read nor write. He spoke in the thick dialect of the Cumberland fells and totally lacked any of the refinements of behaviour or style of his fellows. But this was indeed Lord Henry Clifford.

He was able to prove his case and returned to the Yorkshire Dales to claim his inheritance. But he was unhappy among the splendour of his new life. He preferred the outdoor life and would rather walk by the river than spend time socializing over sumptuous meals. He spent hours exploring his vast estates and had no desire for wealth, opulence, grandeur, pomp and ceremony. During his wanderings, he discovered an old ruined lodge called Barden Tower near Bolton Priory in Wharfedale and converted this into his home. Barden Tower remains today and is occasionally open to the public.

Henry preferred its solitude to his formal home in Skipton Castle but later married and produced his own son and heir. In the meantime, he learned to read and write; he made friends with the monks of Bolton Priory and walked there daily to attend mass, later joining them to be taught astronomy and chemistry. He studied the heavens and the plants of the earth and in time became a very learned and clever man.

The gentle, tranquil Henry, Lord Clifford was loved and respected by all. Unwilling as he was to fight, he was drawn into battle in 1513 at the age of sixty.

He commanded a unit at Flodden Field and his natural leadership skills helped the English to defeat James IV of Scotland. Afterwards, Henry returned to his sanctuary in Barden Tower and lived there until his death at the age of seventy. Afterwards, he became known as The Good Lord Clifford – a well-loved, highly respected and admired Lakeland shepherd who had matured to command knights and yeomen alike.

5   Buttermere

The Beauty of Buttermere

The sad story of the Beauty of Buttermere has been told in many different ways by many great authors. It is a true romance, however, and such is the durability of this tale that it must surely now be regarded as part of the Lake District's folklore. For that reason, it is included in this modest collection, albeit in a simplified form.

Buttermere is the name of both a village and a lake. The lake is one of two which share one valley, the other being Crummock Water. A short distance away lies a third, smaller but equally beautiful lake called Lowes Water. The two larger lakes shelter beneath some of lakeland's loftiest peaks and access to them used to be most difficult. Today, one spectacular means of entry by car is via Honister Pass which climbs from Borrowdale at the foot of Derwent Water and snakes over Honister Hause to drop dramatically towards the calm waters of Buttermere. Another route is via Keswick and over the hills by Newlands Pass, while a third, more roundabout way is from Keswick along the Whinlatter Pass which heads for Cockermouth. Just over half-way between Keswick and Cockermouth, turn south towards Brackenthwaite and Lowes Water, then follow the road along the banks of Crummock Water towards Buttermere. St Ninian is said to have passed this way during his missionary work among the Lake District people.

Buttermere is a small village which becomes very busy with visitors; it has developed into a popular centre for exploring the dramatic fells and towering crags which surround it. There are stunning walks along Buttermere Fells and a superb climb to the summit of Robinson (2,417 foot). One of my favourite ascents is via Sour Milk Gill to Bleaberry Tarn and then to the top of the Red Pike (2,479 foot) or even High Stile (2,643 foot). There are some tough climbs too, such as the ascent of Haystacks with its Innominate Tarn, and Fleetwith with Brandreth soaring above.

From the heights around High Stile, however, one can look down upon Buttermere and at the point where Sour Milk Gill enters the lake, there is a distinct patch of crimson; this comes from residue washed away from the red rocks of those fells and there is a folk story to account for this coloration (see Borrowdale). At times, the water of Buttermere can assume a beautiful green tinge and at other times, it is a smooth silky blue. It is, I feel, one of the most serene of the English lakes and there are pleasing footpaths around its gentle shores.

Flowing from the same range of hills, but running into Crummock Water, is the Lake District's highest waterfall. This is Scale Force which flows from Gale Fell via Scale Beck and, at one point, the beck tumbles between the walls of cliff in one uninterrupted fall of 120 foot. In times of very high rainfall or when the mountain snows are melting, Lakes Crummock Water and Buttermere may merge into one. Many years ago, the two did form one lake and today a fast-flowing stream connects the two, running across land which is very marshy in parts.

In tiny Buttermere village, there is a small church but it is the Fish Hotel which is the focus of interest, especially to those who know the story of the Beauty of Buttermere. At the time of this tale, the inn sign depicted a char, a red-bellied trout-like fish which inhabits the cold waters of Buttermere and other English lakes. Today, the inn's white walls bear two char, a large one and a smaller one.

In the early nineteenth century, the landlord was called Joseph Robinson and he had a daughter called Mary. She was baptised in the summer of 1779 and may have been a few years old at the ceremony, perhaps two or three, but her fame began when she was a teenager. At the time, she was a single girl of remarkable beauty, grace and charm.

With a sparkling personality, she attracted everyone who met her and in 1792, she had the misfortune to act as waitress to a travel writer who was a guest in the hotel. He was called Joseph Palmer, whose pseudonym was Joseph Budworth.

Having visited Scale Force and other popular places around Buttermere, he wrote an account of his visit in which he referred to the glowing beauty of Mary Robinson. He said she was about fifteen at the time and had thick, long dark brown hair which was so beautiful it did not require ringlets. Her face was a fine oval shape with full eyes and her lips were as red as vermillion. He said her cheeks were more the colour of lilies than roses and she had a beautiful graceful carriage which was calculated to set off her dress. A simple girl who had never been out of Buttermere, she captivated this author.

When his article was published, visitors began to visit Buttermere in the hope of seeing this divinely pretty girl and among them were the lakeland poets – Wordsworth, Coleridge, de Quincey and Southey all came to see the girl who was now known as the Beauty of Buttermere. Other less savoury fellows came along too. Her proud dad staged dances and parties, and clearly, with such a pretty attraction for the menfolk, their wives and girlfriends came along to keep an eye on them! Throughout all this popularity and adoration, Mary retained her charm and modesty. She would dance but not flirt, and she behaved in a most creditworthy manner. Joseph Palmer paid a later visit and watched her dance, still marvelling at her beauty and grace.

By the time she was twenty-five, she was still unmarried and working as a serving girl in her father's hotel. She was more beautiful than ever and could have claimed the hand of almost any man, but she remained unmarried as members of the public continued to arrive in the hope of seeing her. Throughout the whole charade, Mary behaved with utmost decorum and patience.

But in 1802, another man entered Mary's idyllic life in Buttermere. He said he was the Colonel the Honourable Alexander Augustus Hope and he was much older than Mary, being forty-four years of age. Expensively dressed and well spoken, he let it be known that he was Member of Parliament for Linlithgow and younger brother of the very wealthy Earl of Hopetoun. He was travelling the country and had just arrived from Keswick, intending to stay for a time at the 'sign of the char'. His arrival was in fact low key; he had no servants and said he intended to relax by fishing for char in Buttermere, potted char being a local delicacy.

This charming, well-spoken gentleman began to woo the renowned Beauty of Buttermere and such were his persuasive powers that Mary agreed to be his wife. Everyone was delighted and they were married at Lorton Church between Cockermouth and Buttermere. The date was 2 October, 1802.

But some people were just a wee bit suspicious of the smooth-talking Colonel Hope. One of them was the poet Samuel Taylor Coleridge. He had earlier encountered Colonel Hope in Keswick and felt that the fellow's behaviour had a ring of vulgarity about it. Coleridge considered his conversation was not that of a true gentleman, being ungrammatical and rough. It was learned that Colonel Hope had been the toast of Keswick for a time, being invited to all the finest houses and he had even proposed to a charming and wealthy young woman.

The wedding had been arranged whereupon Colonel Hope had announced he must hurriedly visit his cousin's country house in Scotland on urgent business. He left, ostensibly for Scotland, but in fact made his way to Buttermere. There he charmed and later married Mary, the local beauty.

Coleridge decided to do something about it and wrote an article about the wedding of Colonel Hope and Mary Robinson. It was published in the London daily paper, the *Sun*. Coleridge did not mince his words. He wrote that 'a gentleman calling himself Colonel Hope ...' had married the Beauty of Buttermere but the paper itself did not believe Hope was an impostor. After all, there was a real man of that name. But the paper soon received a letter from a reader stating that the real Colonel the Honourable Alexander Augustus Hope was overseas, and had been for some time. Clearly, the fellow at Buttermere was an impostor. By Saturday, 6 November 1802, the *Sun* was publishing an article entitled 'The Keswick Impostor' and so Hope's real character was revealed.

He was a very skilful confidence trickster who had lived for many years by cheating. His real name was John Hatfield, born of humble origins in Cheshire in 1758. He had been a commercial traveller and had, in fact, married the daughter of Lord Robert Manners but had spent all her money. He abandoned her and their three children, and Mrs Hatfield later died from her anguish. Hatfield had then established himself in a false life.

He did so by variously claiming to be a member of the Duke of Rutland's family, a Member of Parliament or a highly successful businessman. It transpired that lots of eminent London businessmen had believed his fine manners and voice, and had lent him money, none of which was repaid. His bankers' drafts were always dishonoured and in fact, he had been declared bankrupt. He had also served a prison sentence of seven years in Scarborough, probably for debt. While in Scarborough, he contrived to make himself known to a lady who lived with her mother opposite the prison; she was called Nation and although she had never met Hatfield, he persuaded her to pay off his debts and marry him upon his release. The woman did so. They went to live in Somerset where a child was born, but Hatfield soon abandoned that lady and her child. It was then that he pretended to be the brother of the Earl of Hopetoun. Worse still, that lady was still alive in 1802 which meant that when he married Mary, his marriage was bigamous.

As these enquiries were being undertaken, Hatfield realized he could no longer conceal the truth and fled from Buttermere. He took a ship to Wales from Ravenglass. However, the authorities were awaiting his arrival at Swansea.

Hatfield was arrested and the main charge against him was one of forgery which carried the death penalty; he was also charged with bigamy and various other offences following his fraudulent life. He was committed for trial at Carlisle Assizes, found guilty of three charges of forgery and sentenced to death.

The case received national publicity because of his marriage to the renowned Beauty of Buttermere, but few thought the death sentence would be carried out. Perhaps his cruel deception of the Beauty of Buttermere hardened the judge's resolve because there was no reprieve. John Hatfield was hanged on September 3, 1803.

Instead of allowing Mary to spend her days in peace, the publicity simply brought more people to Buttermere where she continued to work at the inn. She remained for a further ten years, always being courteous to visitors and showing the most exquisite grace in her movements.

Poets and writers now made use of her awful experience and retold her tragic tale in plays, ballads, poems and books. De Quincey, Wordsworth and Coleridge all used her experience as material in their work which served only to increase the number of visitors to the inn. When Mary was well over thirty, however, a man from Caldbeck, another Lakeland village, called at Buttermere while on business, perhaps to finalize a deal involving sheep. He was called Richard Harrison and he was a Lakeland farmer. He met Mary and they fell in love.

They were soon married and this time, the marriage was a happy one. Mary and Richard remained at the Fish Hotel for a while to run it because her parents were too old to cope. Later, however, Richard inherited property near Caldbeck and so he and Mary moved to that village where they farmed at Todcrofts which is in the village, along the road which leads to Keswick. Two sets of staddle stones can still be seen in what used to be their stackyard.

Mary died on 7 February 1837, aged fifty-eight, and is buried at Caldbeck in the same churchyard as the famous huntsman, John Peel (see Caldbeck).

In spite of her very public life as a young woman and her tragic first marraige, Mary made a complete success of being an ordinary farmer's wife and became a loving mother to a very happy family.

6 Caldbeck

D'ye ken John Peel?

From time to time, the activities of a real person, even one who lived in fairly recent times like the Beauty of Buttermere (see Buttermere), can develop into something akin to a legend. Stories of his or her exploits can mature into regional folklore and so it was with the renowned Lakeland hunter, John Peel. Even today, stories of his adventures continue to be told both in print and in conversation and for that reason, I include a brief account of his life within these pages.

The familiar song which made John Peel's name is known across the nation and begins with the lines:

> D'ye ken John Peel with his coat so gray,
> D'ye ken John Peel at the break of day,
> D'ye ken John Peel when he's far, far away
> With his hounds and his horn in the morning.

John Peel hunted the open countryside around Caldbeck and he is buried in the village churchyard, having died on 13 November 1854 following a hunting accident at Ruthwaite. He was seventy-eight years old. His white tombstone, set among other deceased members of the huge Peel family, is on the left just before arriving at the church door; he is not the only famous Lakeland person to lie at rest in this village churchyard.

One of his graveyard neighbours, who died shortly before him, also became the frequent subject of stories and verses. She was Mary Harrison, nee Robinson, better known as the Beauty of Buttermere or the Maid of

Buttermere who died in 1837, only seventeen years before Peel (see Buttermere). She lived at Todcrofts in Caldbeck where two sets of staddle stones can still be seen – these were used to keep cornstacks off the ground and thus free from rats.

Caldbeck lies in narrow, winding lanes to the north of Skiddaw within the northern boundary of the Lake District National Park. The village is full of interest – there is a pond known as claydubs which was probably an early claypit from where clay was obtained for the manufacture of local tiles and bricks; an old brewery was once a fulling mill, and other reminders of a busy industrial past can be seen in several former mills, including corn mills, woollen mills and a paper mill, all depending upon power provided by the stream. Priests Mill is again in working order and is now a visitor centre and mining museum, while the Bobbin Mill, now in ruins, once boasted a huge forty-two foot mill-wheel known as Red Rover. It was dismantled during the second World War and was said to be England's largest water-wheel. That mill made bobbins in wood obtained from local trees. In addition, there is also a clog worker's shop on the main street while the surrounding fells were rich in minerals, thus providing a thriving mining industry which ended as recently as the 1960s.

The church of St Kentigern, also known as St Mungo, is built of old red sandstone and dates from the twelfth century, parts being rebuilt in 1512 with further additions in 1727. It is one of of only eight dedicated to this saint, the others all being in northern Cumbria. Inside on a wall, there is an old engraving of the Nicene Creed, an unusual relic of the Catholic origins of this church. Near the pack-horse bridge there is St Kentigern's Well, said to have been used by the saint during the sixth century for baptising his converts.

Almost opposite the church is the John Peel Memorial Shelter while in the village stands the house where a man called John Woodcock Graves wrote the words of the famous hunting song. Graves was then manager of the weaving factory.

Caldbeck also boasts a beautiful glen beside the stream

which is also called Cald Beck (cold stream); the glen is known as The Howk and comprises a deep ravine worn from the rocks by the action of the beck. There used to be a natural stone bridge across it, this being known as the Fairy Bridge. Today, there is a modern bridge with a splendid view of the waterfalls.

One curious object in the wall near the school is the Spit Stone. For centuries, Caldbeck children would spit on this stone as they passed by; they had to do so without looking back. The origin of this may be that the stone was originally on the ground when it was used as a receptacle for coins kept in vinegar to kill off any plague germs they might be carrying. Spitting has long been regarded as a means of averting evil. Although Caldbeck has so many points of interest, it will be forever associated with Britain's most famous huntsman, John Peel. He was a farmer with six sons and six daughters and earned his reputation as Lakeland's best-known fox hunter because of his addiction to the sport. He was ruthless in many ways, demanding the utmost effort from his hounds, his horse and his fellow hunters. So keen was he that he spent all his spare time hunting, including times when he should have been working on his farm. Yet it seems he was a successful farmer because he was never afraid of hard work.

In fact, his farming had to pay the heavy costs of his hunting and the maintenance of his famous pack of hounds. As the song says, he rose at the crack of dawn whether at work or when hunting but when he was in pursuit of a fox, he obliterated everything else from his mind. He was a true fanatic and although most hunts had ended by mid morning, some did continue well into the afternoon or even into the evening hours with the pack of hounds running up to eighty miles in a day on some occasions.

Much of his hunting was done around Caldbeck although he would venture further away from time to time. Peel hunted mainly on foot; he would ride a small but sturdy Lakeland horse called a 'galloway' and stories circulate which say that the horse knew its master's whims so well that, at the conclusion of each hunt, it would be waiting for its master wherever and whenever he finished for the day.

In his day, the type of fox which lived in and around the Caldbeck fells was called a greyhound fox. It was paler than the reddish chestnut ones we know today and had longer legs and a smaller brush. These foxes had tremendous stamina, speed and courage and Peel was known to allow a fox its freedom if it had provided his hounds and huntsmen with a good day's sport.

Peel had his favourite hounds; they were usually called Britain, this name passing from one dog to another, but the following is a list of the hounds' names, some of which appear in further verses of the famous song: Bellman, Burthwaite, Bowler, Charmer, Crafty, Dancer, Delly, Drunkard, Glory, Leader, Lifter, Lucy, Lilter, Lively, Lofty, Melody, Merry, Ranter, Royal, Stormy, Towler and Welcome. I understand that modern Lakeland foxhounds are still given these names.

In 1832, after a particularly strenuous day's hunting, John Peel and his friend John Woodcock Graves were relaxing in Grave's home at Caldbeck. They were organizing the next hunt meeting. Graves was later to explain how he and Peel were sitting beside the fire, reliving the day's hunting excitements, when Graves' daughter came into the room. She asked about a tune that her granny would sometimes sing. The music was recalled by Graves and, because a pen and ink were conveniently placed on the table, Graves began to write the words of the famous song. it was an impromptu effort and his first words were 'D'ye ken John Peel with his coat so gray'. When he had finishd, he read the words to Peel and the tough old huntsman began to weep with emotion. Graves said, 'By jove Peel, you'll be sung about when we're both run to earth!'

His forecast was to come true. It was the song which has virtually become the Lake District's anthem for it is known far beyond the boundaries of Caldbeck. It was also the marching song of the old Border Regiment. The men of the 34th Foot, who were predecessors of the Border Regiment, whistled this tune while servicing the Light Brigade before the charge at Balaclava in 1854, ironically the year John Peel died.

The song was first sung in the Rising Sun Inn at Caldbeck, but the tune was not the one we know today. It was then sung to Bonnie Annie which was an old Border tune sometimes known as Canny Annie. Another variation is that the original words were in the Cumberland dialect. Graves later translated them into standard English.

For the present popular and very well-known tune, we must thank a man called William Metcalfe, choirmaster and bass singer with the cathedral choir in Carlisle. Having heard the song, he liked it and felt it would benefit from more lively and rousing music, so he wrote a new tune for the song. Being a noted local singer, he was able to perform his own creation and in 1869, some years following Peel's death, Metcalfe first sang the song to his own music at an important dinner engagement in London.

It was at a celebration of the Cumberland Benevolent Association and the song was an immediate and huge success.

It is to Metcalfe and Graves, therefore, that we owe our knowledge of John Peel and it is through them that his name has entered the folklore of the Lake District. Metcalfe died in 1909 and is buried in Carlisle, but Graves had emigrated to Tasmania in 1833. He died in 1886. He was ninety-one years old although his tombstone near Hobart Town claimed he had reached 100. Graves never repeated the success he had earned through writing 'D'ye ken John Peel' but the irony is that John Peel is far better known that either of the song's authors; more surprising perhaps is that Graves did not make one penny from his famous song.

7 Carlisle

Tests of True Love

The red sandstone castle at Carlisle is one of many which, according to legend, were used by the famous King Arthur, Queen Guinevere and the Knights of the Round Table as their home. Of the many tales of Arthur (some of which have been lost for ever), at least two remain which are associated with the Carlisle district. I have related one under the heading of Hesket-in-the-Forest. The Hesket tale is particularly well known, being an account of how the handsome Sir Gawaine came to marry the ugliest of crones. Even that tale has a happy ending.

The second tale is rather unusual, but first I will highlight some of the features of Carlisle, a splendid and handsome town of some 72,000 residents and a long, stirring and turbulent history. There is far too much to be included in full in this modest book and the finest way to appreciate this city is to explore it. It is hoped the following words might encourage such exploration.

With a superb cathedral and a parish church dedicated to St Cuthbert, Carlisle is a bustling city which has endured more than 1,700 years of feuding, wars and border battles. In addition to the town centre (some of it now pedestrianized) there is the new Lanes shopping precinct and many older places of interest.

The older ones include the fifteenth-century Guildhall, the last medieval timber-framed building in Carlisle, which contains a superb museum with special exhibitions in its Guild Rooms. These were once used by medieval trade guilds and the Tourist Information Centre is also housed here. There is another Museum and Art Gallery in Tullie House while the robust castle contains the Museum of the King's Own Border Regiment as well as an exhibition of the castle's own history.

Even the Victorian railway station with its mock-Tudor aspect is of interest to visitors while the Town Square contains a remarkable seventeenth-century sundial market cross.

Carlisle is the county town of Cumbria and its development can be traced to Roman times when Hadrian's Wall was constructed; that stunning wall extended west from Carlisle to Bowness, and east to Newcastle upon Tyne. Much of its stone was later used for other buildings, but the first Roman fort was built here by Agricola when Carlisle was called Luguvalium. The city was then laid out in a grid pattern. Hadrian built another fort which was large enough to house a thousand cavalry members – St Michael's church and some more modern buildings now occupy that site.

Surprisingly little of Carlisle's historic past has survived simply because it has been invaded so many times. Most of its ancient buildings have been destroyed and their stone recycled in further constructions. Even the cathedral's stone was removed in 1644 to repair the city defences.

The cathedral, very convenient for the city centre, is the third oldest in the north of England, being built in 1124, but it is also the second smallest cathedral in England (Oxford's being smaller). Its diminutive size is due to subsidence in the seventeenth century which produced a shorter-than-normal nave. Originally, it was 139 foot long; it lost 100 feet and is now a mere thirty-nine feet in length. Nonetheless, it is a beautiful and interesting church which was originally a Norman priory. The choir is said to be one of England's finest and it is three times longer than the nave! It boasts an exquisite great east window, said to be a masterpiece, and there are excellent carvings.

In the cathedral, there is an early sixteenth-century triptych which was brought from Brougham (see Brougham), a splendid ceiling in the Prior's Room which was restored as recently as 1976, and the undercroft which dates to the fourteenth century.

The castle, built in red sandstone and begun by William

Rufus in 1092, is reached via an underpass under the inner ring road. The keep is twelfth-century Norman while the main gate is from the fourteenth century, these being the most impressive of the existing remains. There is, however, a condemned cell on the second floor which bears lettering carved by prisoners during the fourteenth and fifteenth centuries. The moat once held water and indeed, fish lived here and it was crossed by a drawbridge.

Today, there is a fixed bridge and no water! It seems astonishing that in 1815, the city 'improvers' of the time removed the castle's outer walls and gates and demolished the Great Hall.

Carlisle's Great Fair takes place at the end of August and this is a revival of an older traditional fair which dates to 1352. The Proclamation of the Fair Charter takes place in front of the Town Hall and there are attractions such as a parade, dancing and music.

With its long history of conflicts and turmoil, Carlisle is a fascinating place with a host of further attractions and it is well worthy of an extended visit.

For our story, though, we return to the castle and its ancient links with King Arthur and his knights. It seems that the Grim Baron who features in the Hesket-in-the-Forest tale was anxious to stir up trouble between King Arthur and his lovely Queen Guinevere. He did so by trying to suggest that Guinevere was unfaithful to her husband. This was surely a test of true love. At that time, many of the men and women were far from pure so far as their marital relationships were concerned but in his capacity as King of England, Arthur had to be seen to be above criticism and so did his Queen.

To start the rumour, the Grim Baron sent a boy to Arthur's court in Carlisle Castle. It was the third day of May and the boy carried a magic mantle. This was a long sleeveless cloak worn by the women of the time and the boy managed to win an audience with the king. He announced that, in order to kill any unsavoury rumours about the women of the king's court, each woman should try on the mantle. It was a magic one, the boy claimed, and could only be worn by a woman who was chaste.

We are not given the names of the ladies of the court

who tried it, except that all the knights were somewhat nervous as their spouses slipped on the mantle. One lady, the wife of Sir Kay, did manage to wear it without any problems so at least he could be proud of his wife. But when Arthur told Guinevere to wear the mantle, she was extremely reluctant to do so. Arthur's insistence posed a dilemma but before a crowded court, Guinevere could not refuse.

She took it from the boy and slipped it on. The result was both astonishing and embarrassing. The mantle was ripped as if by magic. It was torn from top to bottom, leaving Guinever as naked 'as shee had been made' and as if that was not sufficient, it began to change colour, first a brilliant red, then green and then black. Arthur was horrified by the spectacle and cried, 'By my troth, I thinke thou be not true.'

Guinevere fled in embarrassment to her chamber, cursing the weaver of this magic garment, while Arthur announced he would deal with Guinevere. He also said would also deal with those who had thought to send this terrible test to his court!

Unfortunately, we are not told the outcome of this curious episode although rumours did surface which suggested that Guinevere's lover was none other than the renowned Sir Lancelot. Was this true, or was it just a nasty rumour spread by the wicked Grim Baron? We may never know.

The second test of true love involves the famous Inglewood Outlaws, Clym of the Clough, Adam Bell and William Cloudesley. The three men, all skilled archers and noted robbers of the king's deer, had been outlawed after being caught stealing the royal venison. They lived in Inglewood Forest in a manner similar to Robin Hood and his Merry Men, although these characters existed long before Robin. They were not unduly harassed by the local sheriff and seemed to enjoy a fairly relaxed kind of outlawry. Two of them, Clym and Adam, were not married, but Cloudesley had a wife called Alice and three children. They lived in Carlisle.

One day, he decided to visit his family. He wished to confirm his love for his wife and by avoiding the city guards managed to reach his home without incident. He had, however, allowed an old woman to live in his house because she had nowhere else to stay and she betrayed him. For the sake of a tiny reward, she sneaked out and told the authorities that Cloudesley the outlaw was in bed at his own home. The delighted sheriff quickly gathered his men and raided the house.

It was impossible for Cloudesley to escape and as the men waited outside, threatening to burst in and kill everyone unless the outlaw surrendered, he pleaded for the lives of his wife and children. They were given their freedom, whereupon Cloudesley decided to make a fight of it. As Alice and the children raced to freedom, he locked the door, rushed upstairs and barricaded himself in a bedroom, intending to fight to the end. But the sheriff had other ideas.

He decided to burn down the house. Cloudesley could not survive such a blaze and so he surrendered to the sheriff who then promised to build him a set of new gallows. The outlaw was pushed into the condemned cell at Carlisle Castle to await his execution as work started on the erection of a special set of gallows in the market place.

But a small boy who worked as the town's swineherd, learned that the gallows were intended for Cloudesley and, because the Cloudesleys had been kind to him in the past, the boy decided to try to arrange a rescue for the outlaw. He crept out of the city and hurried off to find Clym of the Clough and Adam Bell. As he gasped his story, the two outlaws decided to stage a dramatic and daring rescue attempt.

On the morning of the execution, they arrived at the city gates in heavy disguise. They claimed they were messengers sent by the king and were allowed to enter Carlisle but the moment they were inside, they overpowered the guards and tied them up. They took away their keys, making sure the gates were unlocked in readiness for their escape. When they reached the market place, a huge crowd had assembled to witness the execution of William Cloudesley; he was already standing in the cart below the noose. The rope was around his neck and the moment the word was given, the horse would be driven forward; Cloudesley would be left to dangle on the rope until he was dead. Clym and Adam hadn't a second to waste.

In a flurry of well-aimed arrows they killed the sheriff, his justices and his attendants and in the resultant confusion managed to reach Cloudesley and rescue him. Then followed a bloody dash through the mob, with swords flailing, as the outlaws cut their way through the startled people. Citizens were injured and even killed as the desperate three made for the city gates.

It was a difficult dash to freedom, but they succeeded and when they left Carlisle, they slammed the gates behind them and locked them with the stolen keys. This gave them precious minutes to establish distance between them and their pursuers and the outlaws reached their hideaway in Inglewood Forest where Cloudesley was reunited with his wife and family. It seems that peace and security, especially within the realm of family life, now appealed to the three outlaws so they decided to ask for the Royal Pardon for their previous offences.

They arrived in London ahead of the news of their exploits in Carlisle and, supported by the Queen, they successfully pleaded for the Royal Pardon. This was granted, but even as they were still celebrating in the palace, messengers arrived with stories of the bloody rescue. The King was furious but he was a man of his word – having granted the Royal Pardon he could not rescind it and so the outlaws were allowed their freedom. But there was a small price to pay.

Having listened to the messengers' stories of the superb archery skills of the outlaws, the King wanted a demonstration and decided to arrange a contest between his own archers, the Queen's bowmen and the three northern adventurers. But none of the royal bowmen could rival the skills of Cloudesley, Bell and Clym of the Clough. It seems that Cloudesley proved the finest of all, splitting a hazel at a distance of four hundred yards and shooting an apple from the head of his seven year old son from a hundred and twenty yards.

As a result, all three were taken into the King's service and Cloudesley's wife, Alice, became a Lady-in-Waiting to

Her Majesty. Even Cloudesley's children were taken into the royal household and for ever afterwards, the reformed outlaws and their families lived happy, contented and trouble-free lives.

8 Cartmel

Between Two Streams

Cartmel is a small village of grey houses in a flat valley close to the centre of the promontory which lies to the north of Morecambe Bay. It is just over two miles from Grange-over-Sands and five miles or so from the southern tip of Windermere. The centre of Cartmel is very attractive with its pleasing village square, market cross, fourteenth-century gatehouse, village lock-up and rippling stream. One unusual sight is an extension to the King's Arms inn; it rests on piles sunk into the stream near Church Bridge. Not surprisingly, this part of Cartmel is loved by artists and photographers.

Cartmel is also the name of a beautiful priory. As a visitor attraction, it dominates the village to such an extent that a tourist information centre and car park have now been established – the information centre occupies the gatehouse in the village square.

The former Catholic Augustinian priory, one of the few to have survived the Reformation in such a fine state, now serves as the Anglican parish church of St Mary the Virgin and St Michael. Such is its splendour that it is sometimes called the cathedral of the Lakes. It was founded around 1188 by William Marshall who was Earl of Pembroke and Baron of Cartmel and its first prior was William de Walton.

Designed for the Black Canons, as the monks were known, the priory was then called St Mary's, Kertmel or Kyrkmell, and it is regarded as an exceptional example of Transition-Norman architecture. The sheer size and splendour of the priory arises because it was the mother church of a massive area, not merely a parish church for the village.

There may have been an earlier church on the site; Egfrig, son of Oswig, gave the land to St Cuthbert to erect a chapel. However, the priory was successful until the Reformation when, between 1536 and 1537, its Catholic artefacts were destroyed and some of its buildings demolished; its roof was also stripped of lead. Glass from the priory windows, some dating to 1260 but most of it dating to 1400, was taken to Windermere and added to St Martin's Church. During this time of religious strife, four monks and ten husbandmen were hanged because they tried to stop Henry's commissioners taking corn from the Priory barns.

The lovely church, then part of the priory, was spared because it was deemed suitable for the new Protestant faith and so Anglicans began to use the south aisle of the choir as their church. Earlier, between 1300 and 1400, this had been doubled in size with decorated windows being added, hence its subsequent use as a church in its own right.

In 1618, a man called George Preston of Holker Hall restored the main body of that church, but it later fell into further disrepair.

Then in 1859, the Duke of Devonshire embarked on a restoration plan aided by the local people, and this was completed in 1870. Parts of the old church can still be seen, however, such as twelfth-century doorway, chancel and transepts. The stalls and misericords in the choir bear some exquisite fifteenth-century carving and a feature of the church is the splendid Harrington family tomb bearing effigies of John, the first Lord Harrington who died in 1347, and his wife, Joan. The Harringtons were ancestors of Lady Jane Grey who was proclaimed Queen of England in 1553; nine days later she was imprisoned and then beheaded. There are also memorials to people who have lost their lives while attempting to cross Morecambe Bay sands via the low-tide route. A particularly poignant reminder of the dangers of this crossing is a miniature painting of Isobel Crosfield (1747-1821) who is buried here. Her fiancée drowned while making that crossing and the miniature of Isobel was found in his clothing.

Another curious point of interest can be found on the

side of one of the pillars. It is a set of wooden shelves and when I arrived, they contained two fresh bread loaves. When Rowland Briggs died in 1703, he left the sum of five shillings (25p) to be paid every Christmas Day to the sexton and his successors, provided they kept his grave unbroken and left bread out for distribution to the needy of the parish every Sunday – forever.

The income comes from land and the charity is maintained to this day – and the bread smelt delicious! A brass plaque on the pillar gives a full account of this long-standing custom.

The founding of Cartmel Priory is the subject of an ancient Lake District legend. It is said that when the first monks arrived from the continent to build their church, they decided to erect it on a hill at Cartmel. They found a suitable place and started to prepare the site, but as they were laying the foundation stone of their new priory, one of them heard a voice, as if from heaven, instructing them to leave this area. They were told to build their church in a valley containing two streams which flowed in different directions. One had to flow north while the other ran south.

This sounded impossible but the obedient monks abandoned their first site and spent many long months searching the fells and lakes for such a valley. But their search was futile – they could not find such a valley and returned to Cartel, tired and disappointed. But as they crossed two streams in Cartmel, one of the monks realized that they were indeed flowing in different directions, one to the north and the other to the south. And so this was their holy site!

Firmly in the belief that the site had been chosen by God, the monks began work on their priory which became great and successful.

On the hill where their first attempt had been made, they erected a small chapel which they dedicated to St Bernard. It disappeared a long time ago, although the hill is still known as Mount St Bernard.

And Cartmel Priory still occupies a site between two streams which flow in opposite directions. One is the River Eea (pronounced Eye) which flows south through the village, and the other is a narrow stream with no name which flows north. It can be seen on the edge of Carmel village, but it does take a circuitous route to eventually enter the River Eea.

9 Coniston

The Yewdale Giant

The Old Man of Coniston sounds like the name of a giant but in fact it is a mountain. It is the highest, by the narrowest of margins, of several within the Coniston Fells, a range of awesome peaks overlooking Coniston Water and Coniston village.

The lake is five-and-a-half miles long and runs almost north to south, with the lovely village of Coniston built on a hillside beneath the fells close to its northern tip. The village has some striking slate-built houses and was the home of the writer, John Ruskin (1819-1899). He lived at Brantwood, a beautiful house on the eastern edge of the lake and, as a campaigning conservationist, is said to have foreseen the so-called 'greenhouse effect' as a future danger to our environment. Brantwood is open to the public where manuscripts, paintings and memorabilia may be viewed.

The local school is named after Ruskin, and in the village there is a Ruskin Museum with Ruskin Lace on show; this was made by local women to cover his body in preparation for his funeral and the design is based on one brought from Greece by Ruskin during his travels.

The lake has achieved some notoriety as the scene of the death of Donald Campbell. He was driving his speedboat *Bluebird* on the lake while attempting to break the world water speed record. In 1939, his father, Sir Malcolm Campbell, had established a world record of 141.74 miles an hour on the lake. Then between 1956 and 1959, Donald broke that record five times, finally reaching 276.33 miles an hour. On 4 January 1967 he made another attempt to break that record, hoping to reach 300 miles an hour, but the boat capsized and Campbell was killed. His body has never been recovered.

The lake is used for a variety of boating and sailing pastimes and, in memory of the Campbells, it is still used for world water speed record attempts. One historic sailing vessel is the *Gondola*, a steam launch dating to 1859 which has been restored by the National Trust and now takes passengers for short cruises around Coniston Water.

A shade over a mile from the northern tip of Coniston Water is one of Lakeland's prettiest places – Tarn Hows. This delightful tarn is set deep in the hills between Coniston and Ambleside and there are some delightful walks around it. It can be located off the road to Hawkshead.

Between Tarn Hows and Coniston village, however, there is a charming wooded valley called Yewdale. At the head are huge slate quarries, some still in use, and a halt near Hodge Close will be rewarded with a magnificent sight. There is a massive hole in the ground which is a disused slate quarry, and its base is deep with rich blue water. Rock climbers attempt the ascent of these smooth faces from a platform far below; it is an astonishing sight but be warned – it is a very dangerous place.

With two narrow lanes running one at each side of the beck, this is the scene of what is perhaps Lakeland's most dramatic folk story. It features one of the Lake District's giants, a man called Girt Will and in Yewdale there is an elongated mound some twelve feet long which is known as the Giant's Grave. Examination suggests that it is fashioned from pieces of rock and that it was made by human endeavour, but we do not know its date. All that is known is that the Giant's Grave has been part of Coniston folklore for centuries.

To be honest, we might not consider Girt Will to be a giant in the legendary sense. He was no colossus – he was just a very big man, standing nine foot six inches tall and he seems to have been a kindly, but very unfortunate fellow. The name 'girt' is a local word meaning 'great' or 'large' and some accounts refer to Will as Girt Will o' t'

Tarns, which means Great Will of the Tarns.

He was one of several so-called giants said to be living in the Lake District. Others lived near Coniston where two stone circles were discovered in 1842. These became known as the Giants' Graves, for it was believed that real giants roamed the fells from Coniston to Penrith. Some lived in Inglewood Forest and others inhabited the Troutbeck valley.

It is claimed that the last of the Lakeland giants was shot by an arrow fired from the top of Blawith Knott, a small peak to the south-west of Coniston Water.

Girt Will, however, was one of the Troutbeck giants and it seems he came to Yewdale to live and find work. His enormous height made him a frightening character in the simple minds of the country people but Will's happy personality soon overcame their worries. He was accepted and even liked by the people of Yewdale and was given work on the local farms. His huge bulk and strength came in most useful in handling large weighty products such as sacks of grain or bales of hay. He was especially useful in repelling invaders who came over the Scottish border or across the sea from Ireland.

Many bands of Scots and Irish brigands were put to flight by the big man. But underneath he was a gentle, loving character who wanted to have a girlfriend. His great desire was to get married and live like a normal-sized person. But his massive bulk set him apart and although everyone liked him, poor Will could never acquire a steady girlfriend. This lack of romance began to prey on his mind.

At that time, the local lord of the manor was called Sir William Fleming and in his role of defending the valley, he had often to muster the local men to protect the small community. Inevitably, he selected Girt Will and there was mutual respect between the two.

But Sir William had eight fine sons, one of whom would assume the role of knight and lord of the manor upon the death of the ageing Sir William; there was also one very lovely daughter. She was called Lady Eva. Lady Eva had an equally beautiful maid called Barbara who, like her mistress, was extremely intelligent and vivacious, not a bit like the more plain and simple country girls. Both were admired by all the local youths; their beauty attracted would-be suitors from all over the district, and although Eva was betrothed to a young knight, Barbara was not. Even though she was not betrothed, however, she did love a young falconer employed by her mistress's father. His name was Dick Hawksley. She and Dick walked out regularly, and everyone felt that, sooner or later, the handsome young couple would become man and wife.

Poor Girt Will, however, also had his eye on Barbara. His increasing desire for her was doomed to failure and even though she spurned his advances, his obsession began to grow and he persistently tried to meet her in secret. He would stop her for a chat and eventually started to make unwelcome advances and suggestions. As Girt Will's desire grew to the stage of being almost uncontrollable, he became a frightening nuisance to the quiet girl. On one occasion, she was walking home to visit her parents when Will leapt out of the hedge and tried to make her go for a walk with him, but she managed to avoid him and ran off, terrified.

On a later occasion, Lady Eva was riding with Barbara in Yewdale when there was a tremendous noise and crashing in the surrounding undergrowth, whereupon Girt Will burst from cover and tried to drag Barbara away from her mistress. Lady Eva began to remonstrate with the huge man, telling him to behave himself and not to be such a stupid ignoramus, but he ignored her. Now with his temper aroused, there was no stopping him. He wrapped his huge arm around Barbara's waist, lifted her off the horse as if she was a baby, and carried her off.

As he vanished into the thick shrubbery with the struggling, screaming girl, Lady Eva stood transfixed with terror. She felt so powerless but it did not take her long to recover; she galloped all the way back to her father's hall and gasped her story.

Within minutes, a band of Fleming family members and servants, including Dick Hawksley, had mustered themselves and, armed with swords, staves and any other weapons they could find, gave chase. Some were on horseback and others were on foot. In time, they picked up Girt Will's trail and located him as he approached Cauldron Dub. Hawksley called out for Will to stop and put an end to this stupidity, but his appeal had the opposite effect – it galvanized the giant into further efforts. He continued to run towards the Cauldron, still carrying the distraught Barbara. But the effort was too much, even for a man of Will's massive strength and stamina. He could go no further with his burden.

As he reached the edge of the Cauldron, therefore, Will stood above the swirling waters and suspended Barbara over the edge. She was screaming for help for the waters were swollen with recent rains. But as Hawksley and the men approached, Will dropped the terrified girl into the raging depths. She could not swim but in any case the power of the water was so great that she was swept away like a cork. The unhappy Will loped into the hills.

Hawksley did not hesitate. He leapt into the pool in a gallant attempt to save Barbara, but the power of the water was too strong for him. He managed to secure a grip on Barbara's clothes and she enfolded him in her arms as the pair of lovers were swept irretrievably towards Coniston Water. Witnesses said they were carried away with the speed of a galloping horse. No one could help them now.

Even though the Flemings and their friends galloped downstream in their wake, they could not reach the screaming lovers. The terrain was far too rough and as their helpless friends watched in horror, Dick Hawksley and Barbara were swept to their deaths. They vanished beneath the surface as the roaring waters flowed under a bridge. They never resurfaced. Days later, their bodies were found at the edge of Coniston Water, still clasped in each other's arms.

The Flemings and their colleagues did not abandon their hunt for Girt Will; the tragedy of Barbara and Dick spurred them to greater efforts and eventually they caught the giant.

They found him exhausted in Yewdale, not far from where his grave can still be seen. In their anger, they attacked him with swords and clubs; the huge tired man stood no chance and he was killed on the spot. Accounts say he suffered more than a hundred wounds and that his life blood ebbed away like a small brook. After killing him, the Flemings buried him where he fell – and his grave can still be seen in Yewdale.

Cauldron Dub has since achieved the reputation of being a haunted place. From time to time, the ghostly form of a giant can be seen rushing through the woods as if seeking to escape, and when the stream is in flood, it is said that the screams of the dying Barbara can be heard as she is swept away in her lover's arms. Another tale is that two ghostly bodies can sometimes be seen floating on the surface of Coniston Water, each with their arms wrapped around the other.

10   Derwent Water

The Hermit of Derwent Water and Other Tales

Derwent Water is known as the Queen of the English Lakes. This is due to its beauty. It is a magical place which is best seen from a walk on the surrounding hills. Even the most timid of explorers can climb Cat Bells on the western shore, or small peaks like Walla Crag or Castlerigg to obtain superb views of the lake and its islands. There is one walk from Ashness Bridge via Walla Crag and Brockle Beck into Keswick, and it takes in Castlerigg too; a ride on the lake from Keswick to Lodore or the Barrow landing stage will help in the return journey. Worthy of an additional walk is the famous view of the lake from Ashness Bridge along the road to Watendlath (see Watendlath) while a walk upon the shores or a circuit of the lake in one of the water buses can be fascinating. In short, Derwent Water is worthy of an extended visit perhaps with Keswick as the centre of activities (see Keswick).

The lake has generated several folk stories, one of which has led to the Northern Lights, otherwise known as the Aurora Borealis, being known locally as Lord Derwent Water's Lights. The same story also involves Walla Crag and a steep gully which is called Lady's Rake.

James, the last Lord Derwent Water, was a Stuart supporter, and had been captured by his enemies. He was awaiting execution in the Tower of London. Meanwhile his wife was confined to her home on an island in Derwent Water. Today, that island can be seen -- it is known as Lord's Island and is just to the south of Friar's Crag. Lady Derwent Water managed to escape and she took all the family treasures. Very soon afterwards, her captors realized she was missing and organized a search. She knew the lakeside intimately and was aware of a steep, dangerous climb to the top of Walla Crag. Knowing this would give her the start she needed, she used this most difficult of routes and succeeded in evading her pursuers. From the top, her intention was to head for London and use the family treasure in an attempt to purchase the release of her husband.

She failed; Lord Derwent Water was executed for high treason. He was beheaded on 24 February 1716 for his part in the 1715 rebellion, but on the night he died, the Northern Lights gave one of their most spectacular displays. Ever since that time, this brilliant natural phenomemon has been called Lord Derwent Water's Lights while the gully in Walla Crag has become known as Lady's Rake. Most local maps show this gully by that name.

There is an alternative story, however, which seeks to explain why this place is also known as Lady's Leap. It also features a Lord Derwent Water, this time an earlier Lord who lived on Lord's Island in ancient times. He was an evil fellow who was feared and hated by all who knew him. He supplemented his income by robbing and stealing from his titled friends in the neighbouring area. It is said he built a stronghold to contain his illicit treasures and this was in the form of a castle on Lord's Island.

His sister lived with him but she was a good woman. She hated her brother's evil ways and made great efforts to reform him but he refused to listen. Her wishes only seemed to encourage him to greater evils; he would embark upon an expedition of murder, robbery and theft, then would return to regale her with the awful details. Year after year, she bore the burden of her brother's terrible way of life until, finally, she decided to leave him.

One day when he and his henchmen rode off to Kendal to carry out another series of robberies, she set fire to the part of his castle where he kept his plunder. As the fire raged, there was no doubt it would destroy everything he owned, and so, fearing his wrath, Lord Derwent Water's sister ran away. Knowing he would search for her and kill her, she decided to take the most unlikely route.

It involved the ascent of Walla Crag by a narrow, dangerous gully, but she succeeded and managed to leave Cumberland to live in safety with her relations in the south of England. Ever since, that gully has been called Lady's Leap even though it involved a steep upward climb!

Thus there are two versions of this tale, but the maps appear to support the first by naming the gully Lady's Rake.

Another story of Derwent Water also involves an island which remains to this day. It is St Herbert's Island which is roughly in the centre of the lake. It is slightly smaller than Lord's Island, being four or five acres in area. It is named after St Herbert, a saint and hermit who lived there. Very little is known about Saint Herbert other than he died on 13 April, AD 687 and that his feast day is 20 March. He appears to be venerated only in the Lake District but perhaps the best-known aspect of his life is that he was a very close friend of St Cuthbert, once the Bishop of Lindisfarne. It was through that friendship that St Herbert's name is known today.

In the seventh century, Herbert lived a hermit's life on the island which now bears his name, existing on a diet of fish which he caught in the lake and vegetables which he grew around his tiny cell. He was a very quiet and humble man, preferring his own company to that of other people. He enjoyed listening to bird song and loved the solitude of this little island. He had managed to construct a shelter which became known as The Hermitage and it is claimed that its ruins can still be seen. Herbert's cell comprised two apartments, one being twenty foot long by sixteen foot wide, perhaps serving as his chapel. The other was far smaller, probably being his cell.

Nearby, however, towards the end of the last century, a man called Sir Wilfred Lawson constructed a fake cell which he called The new Hermitage and thus some confusion might arise.

It seems that St Cuthbert came to visit Herbert on the

island once every year, sharing his life and prayers but the friendship became so strong that both men died on the same day, albeit many miles apart. It is this coincidence which has kept the story alive. Cuthbert died on the Farne Islands on 13 April AD 687 and Herbert died on his own island in Derwent Water on the same day. St Cuthbert's name is renowned, especially in the north-east of England, and his remains are said to be interred within Durham Cathedral. St Herbert is little known outside the Lake District and it is not known where he is buried.

Herbert's renown as a holy man grew and by the fourteenth century, the parish priest of Crosthwaite and members of his congregation would journey to St Herbert's Island to attend a commemorative mass on the anniversary of the saint's death.

The district had another hermit in more modern times. He was called George Dodd and during the last century he lived in a cave on the side of Skiddaw. Skiddaw lies behind Keswick when viewed from Derwent Water. George was a harmless fellow who eked a living as an artist but he had one major failing – he drank too much liquor. This meant he was often drunk which in turn meant he was forcibly ejected from the local inns.

Sadly, his inebriated condition made him a target for the local ruffians and they often raided his cell and stole his belongings. He died penniless but stories of his presence continue to circulate the area.

11   Edenhall

The Luck of Eden Hall

Edenhall is a village beside the River Eden some five miles north-east of Penrith. It lies just off the A686 between Penrith and Alston and is the setting for what is probably the Lake District's best-known legend, The Luck of Eden Hall.

Eden Hall was a stately home in the village, but the first house was destroyed at the beginning of the last century. It was replaced by a new building in 1821, but this was demolished in 1934 because no one wished to buy it. It has never been replaced. Thus the Eden Hall of the legend no longer exists, although the village is of some interest.

The red sandstone church of St Cuthbert is about a mile from the village along a narrow lane which passes through parkland. With its tiny battlemented tower and with coats of arms adorning the exterior walls, the church is thought to date to Saxon times. The coats of arms belong to the Veteriponts, Stapletons, Hiltons and Musgraves, the latter being owners of Eden Hall and associated with the famous Edenhall Luck, while the miniature tower probably dates to 1450; at that time, the church required protection against raiders from Scotland. There are earlier records, however; Pope Nicholas IV valued the benefice at £24 1s. 4d per annum in 1291 and less than twenty years later, the value had fallen to £6 13s. 4d.

Although the church's origins are Saxon, their work disappeared when the Normans utilized the site but portions date variously from the thirteenth, fourteenth, fifteenth, sixteenth and seventeenth centuries. The gallery is an example of the latter. The bells are ancient too, a pair of them dating to the pre-Reformation period while the stalls are Tudor. The interior is beautiful and outside there is an empty niche on the west wall of the tower – this is thought to have contained a statue of St Cuthbert which may have been destroyed during the Reformation.

The Luck of Eden Hall is a beautiful glass goblet, probably an old chalice, which is some six inches tall. Narrower at the base, the top is open rather like the mouth of a trumpet – indeed, the Luck can be described as trumpet-shaped. The colour of the glass is green and it is richly enamelled with red, yellow and blue. The Luck is at least 600 years old and is thought to have been manufactured by either Syrian or Persian glassmakers around the time of Edward III. There is an engraved leather case to accompany the Luck and this was made by a member of the Musgrave family some 500 years ago. It depicts vine leaves and the monogram IHS (*Iasus Hominum Salvator*), the Latin for 'Jesus, Saviour of Men'. This suggests that the goblet was once used as a chalice during mass, probably being utilized in this very church before the Reformation.

One theory is that a member of the Musgrave family brought it back to England after fighting in the Crusades. It has belonged to the Musgraves ever since, but the Luck is now safe in the Victoria and Albert Museum, London, having been deposited there by Sir Nigel Musgrave. During the last war, it was stored in the vaults of the Bank of England for safety. Those are the facts behind the famous Luck, but the legend varies considerably.

The ancient folk tale tells how a butler who served the Musgrave family went to draw water from St Cuthbert's Well near the church. As he walked silently through the evening darkness, he suddenly came upon a group of fairies. They were feasting and dancing on the grass near the well, and some were skipping in a circle around the glass goblet. This was a sight few people had witnessed because the slightest noise would alarm the fairies and put them to flight. They would rush away and hide, but the butler's silent approach had rewarded him with this delightful experience. He stood and watched for a moment but in a trice, the fairies realized he was there. Acting with the speed of light, they fled. In a matter of seconds, every one had vanished into the vegetation but they had left the green goblet behind. In the urgency of their departure, they had forgotten to take it and it stood unguarded on the grass.

The butler was quick enough to realize the value of the goblet and rushed forward to get it. But it did not belong to him – it belonged to the fairies.

As he turned away with it in his hand, one of them bravely confronted him. The tiny creature pleaded for the return of the goblet, but the butler refused to hand it over. More fairies then emerged from hiding to beg for its return, but the stubborn man refused. Upset and tearful, the fairies departed without their precious goblet, but one of them remained long enough to give this warning to the butler:

> If that glass shall break or fall,
> Farewell the luck of Eden Hall.

The butler gave the goblet to his master, perhaps not daring to keep it for himself due to the threats conveyed in the verse. The responsibility involved in keeping the goblet in perfect condition was awesome for a mere butler. And so, according to legend, it was placed in the custody of the Musgraves. Oddly enough, the luck of the Musgraves did vanish with the loss of their fine home, but the first part of the verse had not been actioned because the goblet remains intact.

As we might expect, there are other versions of this tale. One tells of a warring knight who was returning from the Crusades. He came upon a group of fairies who were making merry by the light of the moon, and when he disturbed them they ran off and left behind a glass cup. The knight took possession of the cup and thus it became the Luck of Eden Hall.

Yet another version relates the tale of a servant who was rushing from Edenhall to Penrith to obtain some leeches. He needed them urgently to give medical aid to his dying mistress. Leeches were used for drawing away bad blood. During his journey, he met an old crone who said that if the action of the leeches was of no benefit, then he should obtain the help of the fairies. He would find them beside the fairy well by the light of the full moon.

The servant went to seek them and found them; they gave him a green glass goblet filled with pure water from the well and presented him with a scroll that read,

> If that cuppe should break or falle,
> Farewell the lucke of Edenhalle.

The story of a glass goblet, bowl or other object known as a Luck is repeated elsewhere.

In Lakeland, there is the Muncaster Luck (see Muncaster) and the Luck of Burrel Green (see Great Salkeld) while in Yorkshire at Burton Fleming there is a similar tale called The Fairy Cup.

Another Lake District Luck is called the Luck of Levens Hall (see Levens), but this does not involve a glass vessel – it relies on a herd of deer.

12   Egremont

The Boy of Egremont, the Horn of Egremont and Wotobank

Egremont is a small market town on the banks of the River Ehen which flows from Ennerdale Water. It is a couple of miles from the Cumbrian coast while behind are the Lakeland hills and Ennerdale Water itself. Although Egremont is not placed among the more popular of Cumbrian towns, it does have its own brand of charm and some points of interest.

It boasts a Friday market, a fine tree-lined and very wide main street with a castle near one end, an interesting church dating to 1195 and lots of quaint, narrow streets with interesting old buildings. Its charter dates to 1267 and there are the remains of the splendid castle on a hill just along the road to St Bees. This dates to the twelfth century and is constructed from colourful red sandstone. The surviving gatehouse is impressive, the tower rises to some eighty feet and the walls are 20 foot thick in places, but the gaunt ruins remind us that the building suffered regular attacks. It was finally destroyed 1578. The sad story of the castle has led to its hilltop site being known as The Mount of Sorrow.

Another old building, restored by local volunteers, houses the Lowes Court Gallery. This is on the main street and exhibits work by local artists; it is also the Tourist Information Centre.

The people of Egremont enjoy some pieces of fun; one is the annual World Gurning Championship. The winner is the person who pulls the most grotesque face while peering through a horse collar! Another piece of fun is the annual Liar Contest, the winner being the person who tells the biggest lie. The story goes that, years ago, the Bishop of Carlisle attended and when he saw what happened during the lie contest, he objected, saying that he saw no merit in the competition and adding that he had never told a lie in his life. For that remark, he won first prize! There are also clay pipe smoking contests in the town!

Perhaps the best known of Egremont's traditional festivities is the annual Crab Fair which takes place on the third Saturday in September. This has been held every year since 1267 but it is *not* a fair devoted to shellfish. The focal point is the apple – the crab apple in fact. There is a parade of the apple cart along the main street at 12.30 p.m. on the day of the fair when apples are thrown for the public to collect. The fair includes traditional events such as sports, shows and hound trailing, but one feature is the famous greasy pole competition. A greasy pole is erected in the street and there is a small sum of money at the top. The idea is to climb the thirty foot high pole without mechanical assistance and so claim the reward. Years ago, a sheep was tied to the top, but money is now deemed more suitable although the chief honour is to climb the pole rather than winning any financial reward.

Another focus of interest is the town's haematite mine which is on the outskirts. This is the last working deep haematite mine in Western Europe and visits can be arranged by appointment. Haematite is a type of iron ore which contains seventy per cent metal, and it is coloured a deep red. The redness colours the surrounding rocks, soil and gravel, and much of the mined haematite is used in the manufacture of jewellery. Jewellery made from the local haematite can be obtained in Egremont.

But it is Egremont's romantic and ruined castle which is the focus of two enduring folk tales. One has its climax in the Yorkshire Dales and is worthy of repetition here, albeit in abbreviated form.

Lady Alice de Romille, a kinswoman of the kings of Scotland, was a noted landowner in her own right, having estates in both Yorkshire and Cumberland. She became the mother of two fine sons but was soon widowed.

This meant that her eldest son was heir to many estates but he also died at a very early age, leaving her second son as the new heir. Upon his mother's death, the younger boy would now inherit vast estates in Cumberland and the Yorkshire Dales. To groom him for his responsibilities, Alice taught him how to administer the land and wealth which would be his; she took him to view the estates and to meet the people who worked for her.

The boy was highly intelligent and quickly learned from his very able mother. Because he had been born at Egremont Castle, probably in the twelfth century, he became known as the Boy of Egremont and some accounts call him William. There are many versions of the tale, some discounting his birth at Egremont and some saying he was not the William who was the actual heir. But the story goes on.

Anxious to show her son the vast Yorkshire estates, mother and boy travelled to Bolton in Wharfedale. During their stay, the young William, who owned a beautiful greyhound, decided to explore the neighbouring woods which covered the hillsides along the banks of the Wharfe. He would be about twelve years old at the time, or possibly fourteen, and as he found his way through the trees, he came to the notorious Strid. This is a point in the River Wharfe where two giant rocks block the flow of the water and force it down through a narrow chasm before continuing downstream.

Such is the volume and force of the water at this point, that it roars through the chasm in the form of a boiling cascade, carrying with it anything that chances to fall into the river. Legend says that many daring youths have lost their lives trying to leap across The Strid, in failing to jump across the narrow space between one rock and another. The leap appears deceptively easy, but in fact it is a killer.

Young William attempted that very leap. He might have succeeded, but as he leapt, he still gripped his greyhound's lead. He had forgotten to release it prior to making his leap and as the boy soared into the air, the dog refused to follow. It remained at the far side, but the small tug on the lead was enough to frustrate William's leap; he failed to reach the far side of the Strid and fell into the raging water between the slippery rocks. His young body was rapidly swept downstream with no chance of survival.

A falconer, working in the woods, witnessed the accident and did his best to save the child, but when he failed he had the terrible task of notifying Lady de Romille. She was devastated and decided to build a permanent memorial to her son. A devout Catholic, Lady de Romille gave the riverside lands to the Augustinian monks of Embsay near Skipton so that they could build a church and pray for the soul of her lost son. Thus they constructed the beautiful priory at Bolton. It was destroyed during the Reformation and the ruin remains beside the river, part of it now serving as an Anglican church. In this way, the Boy of Egremont will never be forgotton.

The second story is called The Horn of Egremont and involves a musical instrument which hung at the gates of the castle. It was claimed that only the rightful owner of the estate could blow the horn; no one else could produce a sound. There are several versions of this story, but this is the one I have discovered.

The story concerns another Lord of Egremont. He was Sir Eustace de Lacy who had a brother called Hubert. It seems the brothers were good friends and both decided to join the Crusades to fight in the Holy Land. Having prepared for the journey, Sir Eustace said to his younger brother. 'If I fall in Palestine, you must return and blow the horn, then take possession of the castle and the estate which will be rightfully yours. In that way, Egremont will not be without a de Lacy as its lord.'

But Hubert was not as trustworthy as Eustace believed him to be, and once they reached the Holy Land, Hubert decided he would acquire the Egremont estate in his own dishonest way. He would ensure that his brother died in the Holy Land, and for this he hired two assassins. He outlined their task – they were to drown Sir Eustace in the River Jordan then return for their reward.

Off went the two villains and eventually they returned to announce their success. Sir Eustace had been drowned as instructed and so Hubert paid them their fees, then continued to fight in the Crusades. Eventually he returned to Egremont, now regarding himself as Lord of the Manor.

Hubert was acutely aware of the legend of the horn, however, and dare not even attempt to sound it. He knew he would fail and so explained his reluctance by telling his staff that he had no right to sound it. He said that Sir Eustace had been lost in the Crusades and said he might still be alive ... he might even return to his rightful place as head of the family. Hubert's friends and servants accepted the story, even though Hubert knew that Eustace was dead. It was a clever ruse, for Hubert realized that while he was unable to produce a sound, it would be known that he was not the legitimate heir.

He managed to avoid every opportunity to sound the horn and as the months passed, his feelings of guilt began to fade. He behaved as if he was the true owner of Egremont Castle, organizing hunting and sporting events for his fellows, putting on huge feasts in the castle and attending to matters around the estate.

Then, many months later, he organized a lavish hunting banquet at the castle and invited all his friends and family. But as the meal drew to a close, he was horrified to hear the unmistakeable sound of the Horn of Egremont. Someone was at the gate and blowing the horn. It could only be one person. Sir Eustace! He must have returned! He had not been murdered after all – he had survived and was now here to resume his role.

In the confusion of that moment, Hubert fled. As the guests rushed out to greet the long-lost lord of the manor, Hubert slipped away by a side door and spent years in exile, wandering around the Lake District and living like an outlaw. A long, long time afterwards, a dishevelled, decrepit old man appeared at the castle gates to beg forgiveness. It was Hubert and the kind Sir Eustace listened to his brother and agreed to forgive him – on condition he entered a monastery. Hubert did so. He spent the rest of his life working and praying with the monks as a penance for attempting to murder his brother.

Yet another old folk tale involves the de Lacy family; it is a grim story. Edgar de Lacy, Lord of Egremont, had a wife called Lady Edwina and one day Lord and Lady Egremont were on the fells near Ennerdale Water. They were accompanied by their servants and the occasion was a wolf hunt. At that time, wolves were plentiful on the mountains and they were a menace, attacking sheep and other livestock like poultry, so they had to be controlled.

As the hunt progressed, it became apparent that Lady Edwina was missing and so a hectic search was commenced. Soon, she was found by her husband – she had fallen from her horse after it had been attacked by a wolf. She had tumbled down a bank into a deep ravine. The wolf had pursued her and as the rescuers approached, they realized that Lady Edwina was dead. A pack of wolves were devouring her body. No one could drive off the ravening creatures and Lord Egremont could only watch as the remains of his beloved wife were eaten. In his desperate sorrow, Lord Egremont cried, 'Woe to this bank'.

From that time forwards, the hillside in question became known as 'Woe-to-this-bank', a name which has been corrupted over the centuries to Wotobank. It is still known by that name.

In the middle of the last century, a ghostly wolf was said to haunt Wotobank and several sheep were found torn to pieces, but late one night a farmer noticed the dark outline of a wolf-like creature and, being a practical fellow, shot it. It was in fact a large dog which had been savaging the flocks, but since that time, there have been no tales of ghostly wolves at Wotobank.

13   Great Salkeld

The Luck of Burrel Green and Dick Whittington's Bells

It is one of the claims of Great Salkeld that Dick Whittington, famous for his black cat, for thrice being Lord Mayor of London, and for turning at the sound of Bow Bells, was born in this Cumbrian village. It stands close to the River Eden and lies to the north east of Penrith, some seven miles distant along the B6412 to Kirkoswald.

One outstanding feature is the well-preserved fortified tower of St Cuthbert's fascinating little church. Although there may have been a church here in AD 880, the tower dates to the fourteenth century; its sheer size and strength implies that it was designed as a form of protection against border raiders. The ivy-covered walls are six foot thick and it is more like the keep of a castle than the tower of a church. The door into the church echoes this stout form of protection while inside are weapons of defence, including a sword, some armour and horseshoes. These were collected after a skirmish between the local Royalists and the Scottish Army.

A spiral staircase leads to a room in the tower which boasts a fireplace and an old gravestone carved with a sword, bell and hunting horn and there are other signs of sturdy isolation and security although the church contains gems like the Norman doorway and a Roman altar, both in the porch. The altar was discovered in the churchyard in 1890 and is a rare find, probably having come from the Roman camp of Voreda otherwise known as Plumpton Wall.

There is Saxon stonework too, as well as other Norman designs, while some of the woodwork dates from the Tudors. There are Elizabethan artefacts, scenes from the lives of Saints Cuthbert and Aiden while the stone figure of a priest is more than 600 years old.

Great Salkeld is the home of two folk talks, with a third nearby at Little Salkeld (see Little Salkeld). One of Great Salkeld's tales concerns a brass dish which dates from the sixteenth century. This is known as the Luck of Burrel Green and is one of several Lucks in the Lake District (see Edenhall, Levens and Muncaster).

This Luck is a brass dish which is heavily embossed; it is circular in shape and is some sixteen inches deep. There are signs that it used to bear two inscriptions, one in Old English around the central ornamentation, and the other upon the outer circle. When an expert attempted to decipher the inscriptions, he concluded that the words were in Latin and that they read, 'Hail Mary, Mother of Jesus, Saviour of Man'.

Although this would suggest the dish has some Catholic origins, there is a legend which offers the story behind the Luck. It is said that this Luck was given by either a witch, a hob or a fairy to a family who lived in Great Salkeld.

An alternative tale is that it was stolen from the fairies who placed a curse upon the thieves should they ever dispose of the Luck.

According to yet another account, it seems that the family who possess it had once performed some act of kindness to the witch or fairy in question and the Luck was their reward. It is a condition of custody that the Luck remains with the house (a farm at Burrel Green).

There is one tale that in 1896, when some occupiers were about to vacate the premises, the Luck fell three times from its shelf. There was no explanation for its fall, but it is now kept in a very secure place so that the occupants will always enjoy good fortune. There is an old verse which says,

If e'er this dish be sold or gi'en,
Farewell the Luck of Burrel Green.

The second folk tale of Great Salkeld concerns Dick

Whittington. Although historians state he was born at Pauntley in Gloucestershire, the son of William Whittington, local legend insists that he was born at Great Salkeld. As a small boy, he was always fascinated by bells and cats, and while he was making his fame and fortune in London, he said he would donate some bells to Great Salkeld Church. Eventually, four beautiful bells were sent by Whittington to Great Salkeld, but they failed to arrive. They reached Kirkby Stephen in Westmorland and it seems that Whittington had expected the parishioners of Great Salkeld to collect them.

But there was a breakdown in communication and the bells were never collected. After a long time, the vicar of Kirkby Stephen decided to install them within the bell tower of his own parish church.

Dick Whittington died in 1423, whereas one of the bells bears the date 1631, so the entire tale must surely be one of pure legend. I know of no authority which says he was born at Great Salkeld either, but as a journalist once said to me, 'Why let the truth get in the way of a good story?'

14   Haweswater

The Submerged Village

England is rich with legends of villages which lie at the bottom of ponds, tarns and lakes but in the case of Haweswater, the story is true. There *is* a village below the surface of this lovely lake.

Haweswater, however, is not an entirely natural lake. It was expanded in 1936-7 to form a reservoir whose waters would serve the people of Manchester. Thirlmere is another such reservoir (see Thirlmere).

The village beneath Haweswater is called Mardale. It occupied a beautiful, remote valley not far from Shap Fell; today, the M6 sweeps within three miles of the northern tip of that same valley, although it now contains a lake instead of houses and people. Haweswater is about three miles long and its southern tip points towards Harter Fell along the valley which is still known as Mardale.

Mardale was considered a very pretty and charming village with an inn called the Dun Bull which was surrounded by rhododendron bushes. There was a pretty pack-horse bridge and village green. The Holme family (see later) built a church here in the fourteenth century but it disappeared long ago and the modern church was not built until 1729. When the dale was flooded the bodies in the churchyard were reburied at Shap.

Mardale Hall was the home of Lord William Howard. He was said to be the inspiration for Belted Will in Sir Walter Scott's *Lay of the Last Minstrel*. There was a prehistoric fort above the parsonage in the village and this remains above water level.

When the village of Mardale existed, its very remoteness produced some wonderful stories. One concerns a small dale leading from Mardale. This is Riggindale whose stream brings a supply of water to the reservoir from the heights of Kidsy Pike and High Street.

Riggindale contains a cave known as Hugh's Cave. The Hugh in question was Hugh Holme who escaped to the north of England in 1209 after plotting against King John. He found himself in Riggindale where he made his home in the cave which bears his name. Hugh liked the district so much that when King John died, he remained in Mardale and founded a dynasty which became known as The Kings of Mardale. The family survived for more than 700 years, ending in 1885 with the death of Hugh Parker Holme.

The family Christian name of Hugh is not the only Hugh to be associated with the lake. At the north-eastern end, in Naddle Forest, is Hugh Laithes Pike. This is said to be the grave of a huntsman called Jimmy Lowther. While hunting one day, he was severely under the influence of alchohol and fell from his horse. He broke his neck and died immediately, which meant he was unable to make his peace with Almighty God.

After his funeral, it was said that his ghost haunted the area to the accompaniment of howls and fearsome groans. Every attempt to lay his ghost failed and so the villagers dug up his remains and reburied them on the highest point in Naddle Forest. His new grave was marked by a large stone and even now, it is said a weird ghostly figure continues to haunt Hugh Laithes Pike.

A further hunting folk tale is associated with Blea Water, a pretty tarn in the mountains less than a mile east of Mardale. Nearby is a crag known as Blea Water Crag but its local name is Dixon's Three Jumps. In 1762, a man called Dixon was hunting foxes in this area. He was on foot which is the traditional means of hunting foxes in the ruggedness of the Lake District (see also Caldwell and John Peel).

While on Blea Water Crag, Dixon slipped and fell hundreds of feet to the rocks below. As he tumbled, he collided with three rocky outcrops, falling from one to the other until he crashed to earth with terrible injuries. Against all the odds, he survived – it is said he was even able to shout to his companions and tell them which way the fox had gone! From that day, the crag became known as Dixon's Three Jumps.

There used to be an odd custom on High Street, a mountain some 2,663 foot which overlooks Haweswater. The odd name arises from the fact that a Roman road ran across the summits of this range, and that road was known as High Street.

The summit of High Street is rather like a plateau and in bygone times, it was the meeting place of the local shepherds. They would partake of sports, competitions and drinking, enjoying such things as Cumberland wrestling, athletic contests, horse races and betting. The purpose of this meeting was to claim one's own sheep which roamed wild on the fells and so shepherds from far and wide would assemble to identify their animals. And while they were there, they made a feast of the whole affair – and it was all done some 2,663 foot above sea level.

It is a shame that the Mardale church lies at the bottom of Haweswater. Before Mardale had a church, deceased villagers were not buried in the dale. Their corpses were carried by pack-horse over the fells via Mardale Common into Swindale. From there, they were taken to Shap for burial, and this route became known as the Corpse Road. Today, there is a footpath over Mardale Common and into Swindale and it gives some indication of the terrible struggle that was necessary to bury one's loved ones.

One old story concerns a murderer who lived in Mardale. Having committed murder, his crime was not immediately discovered and he died with that crime on his conscience. When his body was being carried over Corpse Road for burial, however, there was a tremendous thunderstorm. The horse carrying his body bolted in terror and galloped off with the corpse strapped to its back. The horse disappeared over the horizon and was never seen for three months – and when it was found, it was still carrying the corpse of the murderer. In the meantime, the crime had been discovered and the guilt of the dead man had become known. Some regarded his ignominious funeral charade as a fitting punishment for his crime.

The custom of carrying corpses high across the fells ended with the construction of Mardale's own church in 1729. Mardale is but a memory now but in the years to come, people will relate the folk story which tells of the village at the bottom of Haweswater.

We know it is not a legend. There really is a village at the bottom of Haweswater.

15   Helvellyn

The Death of Charles Gough

My introduction to the Lake District was during the 1950s. As a small boy, I was shown the delights of mountain climbing and when I embarked on my very first ascent of Helvellyn, I was told the story of Charles Gough.

It is a sad but true story which has been told many times but it bears repetition because it has entered local folklore. The story has attracted the attention of many writers, including the great Lakeland poet, William Wordsworth, and the novelist, Sir Walter Scott. They and many others have recorded their versions of Gough's sad death.

The story of Charles Gough is also a story of Helvellyn, one of the Lake District's most intriguing mountains, but more than that, it tells of the astonishing devotion of one dog.

At 3,115 foot, Helvellyn is the third highest mountain in England, being surpassed only by Scafell Pike (3,206 foot) and Scafell (3,162 foot). It stands between Lakes Thirlmere and Ullswater and is one of several very lofty peaks running north to south from Great Dodd to Dollywagon Pike. There are several footpaths to the summit and they begin in a wide variety of places, including Patterdale, Glenridding and other locations along the shores of Ullswater, as well as Thirlspot and further points beside Thirlmere (see Thirlmere).

Some routes to the summit are comparatively short while others are long and even arduous. To reach the top of Helvellyn is a mighty achievement and the attempt should never be lightly taken. To conquer this splendid peak requires careful preparation, the right footwear, suitable clothing, adequate refreshment and a high degree of fitness. There is also the need to inform those whom you have left behind of your intended whereabouts, timing and planned route. If you get lost or hurt, they must know where you've gone and how to find you.

I recall one man who was lost in the spring snows and he was later found dead behind a wall which ran beside the road. He had been only yards away from safety when he had died but no one knew where he had gone; the rescuers had no idea where to begin their search and so he perished. This story, and many like it, reinforce the appeal for climbers to inform friends and relatives of their intended route when tackling this climb, or indeed any other.

Perhaps the most scenic route to the top of Helvellyn is the climb from Patterdale. This takes the climber towards Red Tarn in its basin below Helvellyn and then via Striding Edge to the summit. This was the fateful route taken by Charles Gough.

First, however, a few words about Patterdale. This is a delightful village at the southern tip of Ullswater and it rests in a deep, lush valley also known as Patterdale. Both are named after St Patrick, the patron saint of Ireland. St Patrick is said to have been shipwrecked at Duddon Sands off the Cumbrian coast in AD 540, from where he walked to Patterdale. The parish church of St Patrick, occasionally shared by Catholics and Anglicans, is named in honour of the saint and contains some extraordinary tapestries woven by Ann MacBeth, a local lady who died in Patterdale in 1948. The church, decorated for the harvest festival when I arrived, stands close to the footpath to Helvellyn and there was a sign inside which said 'Helvellyn praises God, but please do not bring it into the church on your boots.'

The prevailing rural Lakeland atmosphere of Patterdale can be gauged by the fact that a mountain rescue post is located here and that sheep dog trials are held annually in late summer. Among the many walks from Patterdale is one over Kidsey Pike; this follows a Roman road over the aptly named High Street (2,663 foot) and this path eventually leads to Mardale at the southern tip of the remote Haweswater (see Haweswater).

Another route takes the rambler to Grisedale Tarn where it is possible to locate a rock which bears an inscription to say that Wordsworth came here on his last walk with his brother; his brother was John Wordsworth, commander of the *Earl of Abergavenny*. John went down with his ship in 1805.

In writing of Helvellyn, Wordsworth said, 'Scafell and Helvellyn are the two mountains of this region which will best repay the fatigue of ascending them.' Like so many others, Wordsworth was captivated by the majesty of this mountain and, after his climb, wrote a poem to an unknown lady to commemorate her first ascent.

From the top, it is possible to see a further twenty mountains, seven lakes and tarns as well as the hills of Scotland and the Irish Sea. One curious monument on the mountain is a cairn which commemorates two airmen called Hinkler and Leeming who were the first to land an aircraft on an English mountain!

Much of the Helvellyn's awesome reputation emanates from Striding Edge. This is a long, narrow strip of elevated rock with a footpath along the knife-thin summit. There are steep drops into Red Tarn at one side and Nethermost Cove on the other. In his *Tales and Legends of the English Lakes* (1891) the late Wilson Armistead wrote that Striding Edge,...rather deserved to be compared to a narrow wall several hundred feet in height, connecting the hill which we had been ascending with the head of the mountain, than to the steep roof of a house. It appeared to us to be absolutely precipitous on each side and the top of the rocky wall was not more than two or three feet wide whilst in some places we could not see, before we came to it, as much ground as would serve to plant a foot upon – the rocks presenting their sharp and rugged edges upwards like slates or tiles standing on end.

It is a fair description of this infamous and dangerous route and it was from here that young Charles Gough met his death. We do not know a great deal about him nor do we know with any certainty how he met his death. What is known is that he was a young man who loved nature and adored the Lake District. He lived in Manchester and whenever he could find the time, he trekked to the Lake District to explore the mountains. He was a regular visitor to the hills where he was known to many shepherds who worked on the heights. Charles was regarded as a very pleasant young man with charm and talent; it seems he was well liked by those who knew him.

One afternoon in the early part of spring, 1805, Charles Gough set out to climb Helvellyn. His intention was to leave Patterdale and walk via the summit of Helvellyn to a hamlet called Wythburn, now on the edge of Thirlmere. There is very little there today other than the church but in Wordsworth's time there was an inn called The Cherry Tree to which he would go for feasting and even dancing. The inn disappeared around the end of the last century when it was covered by the rising waters of the new Manchester Corporation reservoir. It is probable that Charles Gough intended to reach that inn for his night's rest and refreshment. To this day, there is still a footpath between Patterdale and Wythburn via Striding Edge and the summit of Helvellyn.

Although he was familiar with the terrain and the risks of walking in the dark, it was late in the day when Charles set out from Patterdale. In spite of this, he felt he did not need the services of a guide or any human companion because he was accompanied by his faithful dog.

Perhaps he made a mistake in setting out too late upon this arduous trek because the weather in spring is always uncertain, especially on Helvellyn. Another factor is that darkness falls very early. The wind on Striding Edge can be chilling and terrifying too, and driving, drifting snows can obliterate any views below, behind or ahead. When fine weather prevails in the valleys, blizzard conditions can sweep the mountains. Just one of these factors is a danger to a solitary walker; a combination of them can be fatal.

It is possible, indeed likely, that Charles Gough was confronted by freezing darkness, high winds and a severe snowstorm while struggling along Striding Edge because neither he or his dog returned from the mountain. They simply disappeared.

It is known that there was a fresh fall of snow on the day he vanished – high in the mountains, that snow would be severe and dangerous with drifting in freezing conditions. Although the accounts do not tell us what action, if any, was taken to find the missing man and his dog, we can assume that there was a careful search and that his parents and family tried to locate him.

The months passed, with spring turning into summer and late one summer day, a shepherd was working on the high slopes of Helvellyn when he heard the feeble barking of a dog. It was just over three months since the disappearance of Charles Gough but when the shepherd went to investigate the noise, he found an emaciated dog watching over the skeletal remains of his long dead master. Even though the flesh had gone and the bones had been bleached pure white, the shepherd recognized the skeleton as that of Charles Gough because of the clothes which remained. He had seen the young man many times and he also recognized the dog. A notebook belonging to Gough was found beside the body and this provided the necessary proof of positive identification.

It seemed that Gough had fallen 600 foot from Striding Edge because his stick was later found there, but from the meagre remains, it was impossible to say whether he had tumbled to his death or whether he had taken shelter during the storm to later die from starvation, exhaustion or exposure. The theory of a fatal fall seemed the most likely.

It also seemed that the faithful dog had scrambled down the steep slopes to be at his master's side. More astonishing was the fact that the dog had remained there, subsisting on water from mountain streams and any wild creature it could catch for food. There is a good deal of carrion in these hills such as dead birds or rabbits along with the carcasses of sheep and lambs and so the dog would be able to survive. It was known that it had eaten grass too. Rumours said the dog had consumed the flesh of its dead master, but having examined the skeleton, experts totally rejected that theory.

For more than three long months, therefore, that faithful dog had remained at the side of its dead master. The sad remains of Charles Gough were buried in Patterdale but we do not know the fate of his faithful companion. William Wordsworth was touched by the devotion of Gough's dog and immortalized it in a poem entitled 'Fidelity'. Among the lines he wrote is this one:

> This dog had been, through three month's space,
> A dweller in this savage place.

In the October of the year that Charles Gough died, 1805, Sir Walter Scott paid a visit to Wordsworth at Grasmere and the two writers, with a friend called Humphrey Davy, decided to climb Helvellyn. There can be little doubt that they discussed the death of Charles Gough because it had so affected Wordsworth.

Later, Scott also wrote a poem about Gough and his faithful little dog. In it, he referred to Gough as a 'pilgrim of nature'. After hearing the story, but before writing the poem, Sir Walter Scott was walking with another friend, Thomas Campbell who was also a poet. Scott told Campbell the story of Charles Gough and the two men each said it would make a fine poem. Both, in a spirit of friendly competition, said they would produce the better work.

But even on the way home from the walk, Sir Walter was composing the poem in his head and next day sent the first few lines to Campbell. Campbell replied, 'I confess myself vanquished! If I were to live a thousand years, I could never write anything to equal this.' And so Thomas Campbell never tried to write about the death of Charles Gough.

The sad story of this young man's tragic death and his dog's astonishing act of devotion and faithfulness will be forever remembered.

However, there is another reason for remembering the event. It is said that when climbers get lost on Helvellyn, they are often guided to safety by the ghostly barking of a small dog.

16   Hesket-in-the-Forest

A Tale of King Arthur

Hesket comprises two villages, High Hesket and Low Hesket. Low Hesket straddles the A6 about half-way between Penrith and Carlisle with High Nesket now bypassed by the A6. The villages lie along the route of an old Roman road and although there is little of interest to visitors in either of these villages, they have had an interesting past.

The forest from which the area gets its name is Inglewood Forest – Lord Inglewood, the Euro MP for Cumbria and North Lancashire still lives nearby in his splendid home at Hutton-in-the-Forest, the family seat since 1600. It was once a medieval stronghold.

Although the locality is no longer thickly covered with trees, the 'forest' name survives. So thick were the trees in the middle ages that it was said a squirrel could travel from Penrith to Carlisle, a distance of some sixteen miles, without touching the ground. The extent of this huge forest can be gauged by an old verse which says, of another part of Cumbria.

From Lamplugh Fells to Moresby.
A Squirrel could hop from tree to tree.

On Lamplugh Fell there used to be a table which was made from a massive single log; it was said it had been cut from the very last tree in the forest at Lamplugh.

Lamplugh lies some distance away in the western part of the Lake District, between Loweswater and Ennerdale Water while Moresby is towards Whitehaven. This area was part of Thornwaite Forest, one section of the mighty range of woodland which covered the region. Several villages bore the suffix 'in-the-Forest' but in many cases this has been discontinued. For example, the Heskets are more commonly known simply as Low Hesket and High Hesket.

The huge Inglewood Forest was the haunt of the legendary archer known as Clym of the Clough who lived before Robin Hood (see Carlisle). His name comes from Clement of the Cliff, and this outlaw, along with his two friends Adam Bell and William of Cloudesley became the subject of a ballad. Their exploits were as renowned as the later ones of Robin Hood and his Merry Men.

Just like the trees of the one-time forest, much of the Heskets' visible history has disappeared. There used to be a tarn here, for example. It was called Tarn Wadlyn or Wathelayne and its area was about one hundred acres. It was drained and the land utilized for grazing purposes. There was a castle too; it was Castle Hewin built on a hill to the north-east of Tarn Wadlyn but that has also vanished. Another ancient relic between the two Heskets was a flat stone platform with a hole through the centre; a hawthorn tree once grew through that hole and it was known as the Court Thorn. This was the meeting place of the local manorial court but the old tree died long ago.

There is little doubt that the Heskets were busy in centuries past because the Roman road ran between them and carried heavy traffic even in the later centuries. Saints Kentigern and Ninian are said to have visited Hesket-in-the-Forest; the Romans Agricola and Hadrian also called, as well as numerous other travellers, famous and unknown. A hoard of heavily adorned Viking arms was discovered here about 150 years ago, indicating another aspect of local history. The church is about 450 years old and it is said that victims of the Black Plague, which devastated nearby Carlisle, were brought here for burial.

Although Hesket is so quiet today, it does boast a stirring tale which involves King Arthur and his famous Knights of the Round Table. One tale is that Hutton-in-the-Forest, mentioned earlier, was the Green Knight's Castle in the tale of Sir Gawain and the Green Knight. At the time of our tale, however, Arthur and Queen Guinevere lived in Carlisle while in Hesket's ancient castle, there dwelt a huge man. He was ugly, cruel, greedy and vicious and was called The Grim Baron.

Because there are no remains of Castle Hewin, its history is something of a mystery, although it is known that by the time of Henry VIII, it was in a ruined condition. The sixteenth-century traveller, John Leland, referred to it as 'ruins of a castle cawled Castle Lewen'.

In 1884, a historian wrote that the foundations had been visible a few years earlier and said the castle was 233 foot long by 147 foot wide, with walls up to eight foot thick in places.

According to legend, therefore, this castle was the home of The Grim Baron, a man who was twice the size of an ordinary fellow. He had a terrible temper and was extremely ugly. His real name is not known but some theories suggest that the Grim Baron was in fact Ewan Caesario, the giant whose grave can still be seen in Penrith churchyard (see Penrith). It is suggested that there is a link between the name 'Castle Hewin' and his name of Ewan. Could the castle have been called Castle Ewan perhaps?

Whatever his name, the Grim Baron took everything he wanted – cattle, crops, food – and the people were terrified of him. The fair maids of the district were especially fearful because whenever he wanted the companionship of a woman, he would kidnap one of them and carry her off to his lair. Lots of them never emerged from the castle after his ill-treatment and abuse, but one very spirited girl did manage to escape while the Baron was hunting.

It was New Year's Day and in her sorry state, she fled to Carlisle to seek the help of the renowned King Arthur. She wanted the Baron to be punished for his crimes and prevented from attacking any more maidens.

King Arthur, having taken vows of chivalry, dressed in his finest suit of armour, took up his most precious sword and rode off to tackle the wicked Baron. For some reason, he was not accompanied by his band of gallant knights and set off alone. It was not an easy journey; it was winter time and the ground was covered with snow. The bare trees of Inglewood Forest had branches like tentacles and the undergrowth was almost impenetrable but after struggling for six tough miles the determined Arthur reached his destination.

He arrived at the edge of Tarn Wadlyn and there, across the lake, he could see the castle on its hilltop site. Rather nervously, Arthur approached the castle for it seems it stood on magical ground. The Grim Baron was able to exert a strange power because as Arthur marched towards the forbidding building, he suddenly found that his strength had vanished. His courage failed too and his sword arm was useless, hanging by his side like a limp piece of vegetation. For the first time in his life, the powerful King Arthur was helpless and as he pondered his next move, the Grim Baron appeared and began to laugh at him.

Having turned the mighty Arthur into little more than a plaything, the Baron said he would spare Arthur's life and permit him to return to Carlisle because he was no longer a threat. Then the Baron added, 'If you want your strength back, you must return to Castle Hewin next New Year's Day with the answer to this question – what is it that a woman loves best?

If you can truthfully answer that question, your strength and courage will be restored.'

Arthur had no alternative but to obey so he returned to his castle in Carlisle, a sorry sight. When his knights saw his condition, they offered to storm the castle and deal with the Baron, but Arthur refused their offer. He was worried that they might also be stricken in this way. For the following months, therefore, he visited his advisers and health experts, asking if they could cure him, but none could.

They tried every known remedy, but Arthur remained a weak and frightened man. He also called upon his Queen and the most intelligent ladies of her court, asking if they could provide the answer to the Baron's strange question. But none could. All through that year, King Arthur remained a sick man, growing morose and depressed because neither did his illness improve nor could he find the answer to the Baron's riddle. And all the time, the next New Year was rapidly approaching.

Then on Christmas Eve, Arthur decided to ride into the fells and spend time alone with his thoughts. He needed peace and quiet so that he could reflect on all that had occurred during the past twelve months. He might even find the elusive answer to the Baron's question. As he rode high into the fells, though, he was compelled to find shelter from a fierce blizzard which suddenly erupted. It threatened to blind him and his horse, so he rode towards the lower ground as he struggled through the white blanket of ever-deepening snow.

He was having difficulty controlling the horse with just one good arm when he came upon a cave in the hillside. Thankfully, it was large enough for both him and his horse and they entered with enormous relief. As his eyes grew accustomed to the gloom, he realized there was someone else in the cave – an ugly old woman seated on a pile of straw. She was trying to light a fire to provide a little warmth and so Arthur gave assistance by finding some dry leaves and twigs.

Soon, in spite of his weak arm, he had a fire blazing and only then, in the light of its flickering flames, did he realize how horrible she looked. Her body was hideously deformed, her arms and legs like sticks, her face the most repulsive he had ever seen, she had blackened teeth, warts all over her skin and a pair of pale, staring eyes. She was dressed in smelly, dirty rags and wore nothing on her filthy feet. Outside, the snow was falling heavily and so the King had no alternative but to remain. He settled down beside the fire as the old crone fixed him with one of her awful stares then she asked why his arm dangled so helplessly.

Arthur told his story; he related how the Grim Baron had mysteriously taken away all his strength and courage, and how the fellow had presented him with a strange question which must be answered on New Year's Day. Having heard his story, the crone said, 'If you will promise that one of your handsome young knights will marry me, I will tell you the answer to that riddle.'

Arthur looked at the horrible old woman and knew that no young man in his right mind would ever contemplate such a union, but if his strength was to be restored, then he must persuade one of them to do so. Risking all, he said, 'I will ensure that one of my knights becomes your husband.'

'In that case,' beamed the ghastly old creature. 'I will provide the answer to your riddle. You ask what is it that a woman's loves best? and the answer is, woman best loves her own free will. That is the answer to the Grim Baron's question.'

When the blizzard ceased, Arthur returned to his court but he was afraid to reveal the promise he had made to the old crone. He decided that he must first confront the Baron and so he returned to the Castle Hewin on New Year's Day. The Baron emerged to meet him. 'Well, did you find the answer to my question?' he chortled.

'I did,' said Arthur, and answered in the words given to him by the old crone.

At first the Baron was furious, but when he calmed down he agreed that it was the correct answer and immediately, Arthur's strength and courage returned. Arthur then told him of the reason for his original visit and the Baron, now faced with a powerful King Arthur, agreed to be kinder to the local people and not to kidnap any more maidens.

Arthur said he would keep in touch with the local people to ensure the Baron kept his word. In the years which followed, he did become much kinder and more tolerant of his neighbours.

Having dealt with the Baron, Arthur now had the delicate, if not impossible, task of persuading one of his knights to marry the old crone. Now that his bravery was restored, he felt able to present the request to them. He assembled them for dinner at the famous round table and over glasses of fine wine, related his adventure which included a vivid description of the old woman and the question she had answered for him. When he came to the crone's request that one of them must marry her, he expected a rebellion. But one loyal knight, Sir Gawaine, said, 'Sire, if you desire one of your knights to undertake that task for the good of all, then I shall do so.'

Gawaine was a fine and trusty fellow, the eldest son of King Lot, the King of Lothian, Orkney and Norway. He was one of Arthur's best known knights, receiving his knighthood from no less a person than the Pope during a visit to Rome. In the Arthurian legends, Gawaine has been married many times to many different ladies, including the daughter of the giant Carl of Carlisle, but in this story he volunteered to be wedded to an ugly old creature. Once he had agreed, the marriage was arranged.

The old crone, grinning in her rags, was brought to the church in the castle where Sir Gawaine awaited. He and Arthur talked briefly before the ceremony, but the bold knight was steadfast – he had made a promise to his king and the marriage would take place.

And so the unlikely couple were united in holy wedlock but when the marriage was consummated that night, a remarkable transformation occurred. Quite suddenly, the old crone turned into a most beautiful young woman.

She had exquisite dark eyes, rose-coloured cheeks, a stunning figure and a delightful sense of humour. Sir Gawaine was astonished, but then his bride explained that, when she was young, she had had a wicked stepmother who was extremely jealous of her beauty. She had cast a spell which turned the girl into an ugly old crone until the right knight came along. But there remained one more test for Sir Gawaine.

His bride warned him, 'I am beautiful only by night; in the morning, I shall return to my image of the old crone unless you truthfully answer a question.'

'I will do my best,' promised Gawaine.

'This is the question,' she said. 'Do you prefer me to be beautiful by day or by night?'

'You are my lady and my wife,' smiled Gawaine. 'That means you shall have your own will.'

'That is the answer I needed,' she sighed with relief. 'It means the spell is finally broken and I shall be beautiful both by day and by night.'

And, like all good stories tell us, they all lived happily ever after.

However, it seems that the Grim Baron had not finished with King Arthur. Determined to stir up trouble between Arthur and Guinevere, he sent a magic garment to Arthur's castle; it could only be worn by chaste women –

and the Baron wanted Arthur to see if Guinevere could wear it! (For that tale, see the chapter on Carlisle.)

17 Keswick

The Druids' Circle

The market town of Keswick is a former mining community which has developed into a thriving tourist centre. With so many mountains and lakes nearby, it attracts millions of visitors, some of whom are content to sightsee in and around the town while the more energetic prefer to climb the mountains, explore the fells or enjoy lively sport on Derwent Water (see Derwent Water).

Established near the northern tip of Derwent Water and beneath the huge bulk of Skiddaw, Keswick is the capital of northern Lakeland and is rich with interest. The old Moot Hall on an island in the middle of Keswick's traffic, looks rather like a church. This is because of the building's style with its clock tower at one end. The Tourist Information Centre is located here but take a close look at the old clock – it has only one pointer, the hour hand.

The town was popular with the Lakeland poets – Southey, Shelley and Coleridge once lived here while Wordsworth, De Quincey and Ruskin were regular visitors. The Fitz Park Museum contains some of their manuscripts as well as a remarkable collection of minerals including a huge type of xylophone made from 'musical stones'.

This is the Rock, Bell and Steel Band of Joseph Richardson and comprises sixty stones, sixty steel bars and forty bells; the longest stone is more than a yard long while the smallest bell is a mere two inches or so. Four people are required to play this curious instrument. In addition, there is a railway museum at the former railway station while the Cumberland Pencil Factory also boasts its own museum and display of pencil art. The world's first lead pencils were made here.

Craft workers sell their beautiful products in many of Keswick's shops and The Guild of Lakeland Craftsmen stages an annual exhibition at Old Windebrowe during the summer. Other entertainment includes a cinema and the mobile Century Theatre which stages performances in the car park near the lake. A riding centre, annual agricultural show, religious festivals and varied water activities are all part of Keswick's busy scene.

One of the finest of Lakeland views is a short walk from the town centre. Little more than half a mile south of Keswick, along the road to the lake, there is Friar's Crag. This is a rocky promontory which juts into Derwent Water and provides beautiful views across the lake towards Borrowdale and the surrounding mountains. The crag supports a monument to one of Lakeland's saviours, Canon Hardwicke Drummond Rawnsley. He was once vicar of Great Crosthwaite on the edge of the town. It was Canon Rawnsley who, with Miss Octavia Hill in 1895, founded the National Trust.

Their foresight and determination have provided the means by which much of the Lake District has avoided unwelcome development. Many unspoilt areas owe their security to Canon Rawnsley and Octavia Hill, and today the National Trust owns and cares for thousands of acres around the Lake District.

Near Friar's Crag there is also a monument to John Ruskin, the noted writer and critic who claimed that the view from Friar's Crag was among the three most beautiful in Europe. Ruskin lived near Coniston (see Coniston).

Some three miles north of Keswick, where the A66 sweeps north along the eastern shores of Bassenthwaite Lake, there are the villages of Braithwaite and Thornthwaite. Thornthwaite is just off the A66 some two miles from Keswick along the road to Cockermouth. In Thornthwaite there is a famous hotel called The Swan.

Perched precariously on the slope of the fells above the hotel is a curious white-painted rock called The Bishop or The Bishop of Barf. It is visible from a great distance and can clearly be seen from the other side of Bassenthwaite

Lake. Some believe that the outline of the rock resembles the robed figure of a bishop, hence its name, but there is another reason for referring to this rock as The Bishop.

The story goes that in 1783, the Irish Bishop of Derry, now Londonderry, came this way. He was *en route* to Whitehaven, which was then the main port to Ireland and stayed for a while at The Swan.

It seems he must have sampled the quality of the local ale because he wagered the locals that he could ride over the steep-sloped mountains on his horse via Barf (1,536 foot) and reach Whitehaven by that direct route. The wise local people said it was impossible – the face of the fell at this point is almost perpendicular and is almost impossible for a man to climb, let alone a horse. Undaunted by their remarks, however, and perhaps fortified with beer and a little faith, he set off in great spirits upon his horse. He managed to get only half-way up Barf towards Lord's Seat (1,811 foot), which is the mountain behind the Swan. At that point, where the white painted rock now stands, horse and rider fell to the foot of the scree and both were killed instantly. The bishop and his horse were buried where they fell, at the foot of the scree. It is said the bishop was the first and last person to attempt rock-climbing on horseback!

The rock from where they fell is now painted white and acts as a landmark as well as a memorial to the dead bishop. At the foot of the scree is a small stone which marks their grave – this is called the Bishop's Clerk.

There is a curious custom which says that the first person to repaint the rock white in the springtime, will receive the sum of five shillings (25 pence) and a quart of ale from the landlord of The Swan, although the present rate for this work is negotiable!

When I arrived, the bishop had received his new white coat of roadmarking paint only a week earlier. It had been painted by the Corps of Royal Engineers from Cheshire and they also repainted the Bishop's Clerk. This is now a regular challenge for the Corps who first painted the Bishop in 1987 to celebrate the 200th anniversary of the regiment's formation. It is not an easy task but the reward was four pints of beer for each soldier and the inn now displays photographs of their work.

Keswick has much more of interest. One popular viewpoint is the summit of Castle Head which is a pleasant walk from the town. The climb to the top of this tiny, redundant volcano is just over 500 foot, but it offers splendid views of the lake and mountains.

Just over a mile from Castle Head is Lakeland's most important and most ancient relic. This is the renowned Castle Rigg Stone Circle which stands about two miles out of Keswick, just off the A66 road to Penrith. The stones are, in fact, beside the old road to Penrith which now forms a minor lane between two points of the new A66. The precise age of the circle of stones is unknown. Some authorities claim it was constructed around 1400 BC, others claim it is more than 7,000 years old, some believe it is the work of Stone Age or Bronze Age Man, while others believe it is linked to the religious ceremonies of the druids. Today, there is public access, for it is owned by the National Trust albeit under the care of the Department of the Environment.

Thirty-eight huge stones remain to form a rough oval shape rather than a true circle and the complex is a shade more than 100 foot in diameter. It is unique because it has an additional enclosure, within the circle, of a further ten stones set in a rectangle. Some call this 'the vestry', and it is thought the circle was utilized by the early Christians for some of their religious ceremonies. The tallest of the stones rises to about seven foot but most are much shorter, some only three or four foot high but most are erect.

Within the circle are pairs of stones which point to the rising sun both at midsummer and in midwinter but how did they get here and what was their purpose? These questions continue to puzzle visitors. It has been shown that if a straight line is taken through the original central circle towards Fiends' Fell in the Pennines (a north-easterly direction), it passes through Lakeland's other famous stone circle, the one which boasts a tall stone known as Long Meg (see Little Salkeld). This line also happens to indicate the direction of the rising sun on 1 May.

The odd and somewhat remote location of the stone circle together with its mysterious shape and purpose has given rise to stories and myths, the best known being perhaps the tale of the two lovers, Mudor and Ella. According to the story, the young couple lived during pagan times when the druids were their priests.

In order to appease their various gods, which included the sun, the druids offered many live sacrifices and some were human. The focal point of their ceremonies was a massive circle of stones built on a flat, elevated site near the convergence of two Lakeland valleys. Today, those valleys contain Derwent Water to the east and Thirlmere to the south-west.

From here, they worshipped the sun and their other gods, believing that certain plants, like the mistletoe, were magic and holy. At that time, the landscape around the circle was covered with leafy woods and these produced an abundance of oak, also regarded as a holy tree. The oak provided them with mistletoe as well as shelter both in summer and winter and so a thriving community of people developed around the stone circle. The circle was the centre of their world – the sacrifices offered from there made sure that their gods were appeased.

Mudor and Ella were children of this community. Even as youngsters, they had played together, exploring the woods, swimming in the nearby Tewet Tarn or the cool streams, searching for birds' eggs or just picking flowers. As they matured, their friendship developed into love and they decided they would spend their future lives together. Neither had any wish to leave the community nor to court the love of any other person. In short, Mudor and Ella were made for one another.

As the couple matured and began to plan their future together, the small community fell victim to a terrible plague. This swept through the village. It was a raging illness accompanied by high fever and soaring temperatures. Within days, several people died and so the druids decided that the only solution lay in prayerful guidance from one of their most powerful gods. As a result, the archdruid was sent to a neighbouring community which boasted the majestic carved figure of the god Mogan. The archdruid was to pray for guidance by offering the golden bough (the mistletoe) to Mogan, so off he went. Kneeling before the terrifying figure of Mogan, the archdruid presented his gifts, completed his rituals and waited for an answer to his problem.

In time, the answer came. He was told that the plague was a form of punishment from the gods; it was in retribution for the wicked misbehaviour of the people but reparation could be made. When the archdruid asked in what form such reparation must be, he was told that a virgin must be sacrificed by fire. That was the only way to appease the angry gods and once they had been satisfied, the plague would come to an end.

The archdruid returned with a heavy heart. He was well acquainted with all the families and their children and was faced with the terrible problem of selecting one young girl as a human sacrifice. After discussing it with the people, it was decided that a lottery was the only suitable method – each girl would pick a wild flower; each flower must be different from any other and all would be placed into a large container. The archdruid would then blindfold himself to draw out just one flower. The virgin who had placed that flower into the container would be burnt alive as their sacrifice.

On the day of the selection, all the druids gathered in that part of the stone circle which is still known as the vestry. It was decorated with mistletoe and oak, flares burned at each corner and as the robed druids awaited, the young girls came forward with their flowers. One by one, they placed them in the deep wooden receptacle.

When the time came for the archdruid to reach deep inside to extract just one flower, all the mothers were weeping with fear and their daughters clung to them as the fathers and sons tried to appear brave. Amid a great chanting, the archdruid dipped his hand into the mass of flowers and pulled out just one – it was Ella's.

Her mother fainted as her husband tried to comfort her, but Ella herself remained calm and dignified. She had already accepted the fact that if she was selected, she would meet her fate with composure. If the gods had selected her to save her people, she would not flinch from her task.

Mudor thought otherwise. He flew into a rage and

beseeched the druids to reconsider their choice. He argued that there must be other ways of selecting the sacrificial virgin, that the gods would never choose such a young and beautiful girl for such a terrible end, but the sombre druids were not moved. 'The gods have chosen Ella in this way,' they said. 'It is beyond our powers to alter their choice. This is an irrevocable decision. Ella will be our fire sacrifice.'

Mudor was devastated. He spent the next few hours in an agony of mind while the brave Ella showed her determination to meet her destiny with calmness and even devotion. She knew that her sacrifice would save her village from the plague and felt a deep, it fearful, pride in what was about to happen to her.

On the day of the sacrificial offering, the villagers gathered for the ceremony. Ella was dressed in a long white flowing robe and placed on a seat which was carried by six young men on a flower-decorated platform. A procession was formed with all the robed druids at its head; then followed Ella and behind her came her family, then Mudor and his family, and finally all the other villagers. They marched to the circle of stones where the druids chanted their offices, with Ella sitting on her platform in the centre of the vestry. When those rituals were over, she was carried on to the place of sacrifice.

This was deep in the woods beneath a crag of overhanging rock. It was a shallow cave in the cliff face above the River Greta, a sort of grotto, and it was almost hidden by the overhanging branches of the holy oak trees. In the entrance there was an elevated piece of flat, circular rock and beside it stood several tall stones. This was the sacrificial altar.

The druids picked garlands of oak with which to crown their heads and the people gathered around to watch, some climbing into the sturdy oaks to secure a better vantage point. A team of helpers then brought forward a basket-work cage with a door opening at one side. It was placed on the circular rock with its sides resting against the stone uprights and its door open and facing the assembled druids. They began to chant one of their hymns as the beautiful young woman was brought forward.

Garlands of oak and mistletoe were placed upon her head, around her neck, wrists and ankles, and then she was led towards the cage. Two older priests supported her for she was now trembling with fear and the entire gathering began to sing their hymn to the sun. As the singing intensified, Ella was placed inside the basket-like cage and the floor area was then covered with layers of dry leaves, grass and small sticks.

It was the custom that every one of the onlookers had to supply one stick; they had to come forward and place their offering of a stick within the cage so that it would make a larger fire to consume the victim. When everyone had made a contribution, the archdruid produced two large, dry sticks and began to rub them together so that the friction would produce a flame. As he worked, he sang another hymn to the sun and soon the sticks were smouldering. Within minutes, they were ablaze and he thrust them into the cage with its tinder dry materials. The door was closed and secured as onlookers sighed and wept; quickly, the tiny flames grew larger as dense smoke concealed the cage and its encased victim.

But Mudor had not been idle. He had prayed to his own god and as the flames rose and crackled, and as the voices of the congregation rose to a crescendo in that horrible woodland cavern, a crack appeared in the rock above the burning casket. Miraculously, a surge of water poured out. Then other cracks appeared and more streams gushed from the rocks; most of them spouted upon the burning casket and within seconds, the flames had been extinguished. In moments, the floor of the cave was awash with the rising water as Mudor rushed to open the cage.

Ella, her hair and face singed but otherwise unhurt, staggered out as Mudor helped her to safety; both were weeping with joy and relief as the congregation looked on with amazement. No one was sure what to do next, but the archdruid took command. 'This is a sign from the gods,' his voice boomed across the woodland. 'Human victims are no longer to be tolerated ... Ella shall be freed.'

From that day, there were no more human sacrifices and the cult of the druids drew to a close. Mudor and Ella lived happily together into old age, but it is said that even today, that rock in its secret place above the River Greta sometimes opens to produce gallons of pure fresh water.

18   Kirkby Lonsdale

The Devil's Bridge

Kirkby Lonsdale (with a population of 2,300) is a small and very attractive market town on the south-eastern outskirts of the Lake District. With lovely old buildings, Georgian houses, quaint narrow streets, some interesting squares and an air of quiet charm, it nestles in the foothills of the Pennines. It also boasts a Tudor grammar school and a 600-year-old cross in a tiny square at Mill Brow, along the footpath to the riverside.

To the west are the familiar shapes of the Lakeland hills with the Irish Sea beyond. The busy A65 (Skipton-Settle-Kendal road) passes through Kirkby Lonsdale from south-east to north-west, while the north-south A683 road from Sedbergh to Lancaster crosses the A65 near the town. I found an old stone milepost saying, 'London 250, Settle 17, Clapham 11, Ingleton 7' while in the hills beyond are some Stone Age graves and the remains of a Roman camp.

The lovely River Lune flows through Kirkby Lonsdale on its way from the Westmorland fells to Morecambe Bay and it was a view across this river from the high bank beyond the church, that inspired the artist Joseph Mallord William Turner (1775–1851) to paint it. He so enthused about the panoramic view towards Howgill and Casterton Fell that he persuaded the writer John Ruskin to pay a visit.

Ruskin did so in 1875 and said, 'The valley of the Lune at Kirkby Lonsdale is one of the loveliest scenes in England – therefore in the world. I do not know in all my own country, still less in France or Italy, a place more naturally divine.'

Since that time, that vantage point has become known as Ruskin's View and access is gained through the churchyard via a well-signposted route. Seats are provided, although it must be said that Ruskin added that the town had moorland, a sweet river and a forest which were at their best in his time.

The parish church of St Mary the Virgin in Kirkby Lonsdale is noted as the finest in the district and is said to be the best example of a Norman church in Cumbria. Although it has been altered a great deal throughout its long history, the most recent occasion being in 1866, some twelfth-century columns remain and other surviving Norman items include doors and windows. Some of the pillars bear diamond-shaped patterns which are similar to those in Durham Cathedral, something which puzzles the experts, and the old church contains many other treasures. Part of a screen, for example, is more than 500 years old, while a piscina niche in a pillar of the south arcade is more than 700 years old. The carved oak pulpit bearing the date 1619 was originally a three-decker but was reduced in size in 1866, but such was the importance of preaching that in the eighteenth century one of the pillars was removed to allow the congregation a better view of the pulpit!

One memorial is to a local man called William Sturgeon who died in 1850; he achieved recognition for his studies of thunderstorms.

During the last century, there was a legend surrounding a buried church. It seems that somewhere near Kirkby Lonsdale there was a hollow in the ground, rather like a huge scooped-out saucer. The story was that a church once stood there when there was a terrible earthquake. Mass was being said at the time and the church was full. Church, churchyard and congregation all vanished as the earth closed over them. Until the last century, it was said that if anyone went to that eerie place on a Sunday morning, it was possible to hear the church bells ringing for mass (see Kirkstanton).

One of Kirkby Lonsdale's proudest assets is a medieval bridge just off the A65 at the Skipton end of the town and within easy walking distance. Known as Devil's Bridge, it no longer carries traffic and is listed as an ancient monument. It is a popular attraction for residents and visitors alike and there is a lovely riverside walk between this bridge and the town centre. When I arrived, the river was in flood, the rushing brown waters adding to the majesty of the scene. The car and coach parks were full, and ice-cream vans and mobile snack bars were busy because of the rock-strewn riverside beneath and the accessibility of the river banks.

There is no doubt that the graceful bridge in this most romantic of settings, with three ribbed arches forty foot above the water, has become one of the most photographed in the area but its date of construction is unknown. There is proof, however, that the bridge was repaired more than 600 years ago, hence it is known to have existed in the fourteenth century. It is known to have been there in 1365 when a grant of pontage was awarded to the vicar, pontage being a toll paid by travellers and then used to maintain the bridge. In 1673, someone inscribed a warning which can still be seen on a short pillar near the parapet of the bridge – it exhorts all who pass over it to 'Fear God and Honour the King'.

For centuries, the bridge was used by foot and horse traffic alike. It carries a very narrow thoroughfare and was once even narrower, so much so that it has been said that 'two wheelbarrows trembled if they met'. If two normal sized horse-drawn vehicles wanted to cross from opposite directions, one had to wait until the other had completed the crossing. Small recesses are built into the parapets so that foot passengers could step aside to allow the passage of carts and coaches.

A nearby modern bridge, built in 1932, carries today's heavier motor traffic along the A65 but it is pleasing that the town authorities have decided to retain the old structure. Our lack of knowledge of the origin of the old bridge has led to the legend from which it gained its name, Devil's Bridge. This is supported by a curious mark in the stonework which is said to be the Devil's footprint.

According to the tale, an old lady from Kirkby Lonsdale was moving one of her cows and a pony, and she needed to cross the River Lune at this point. Here, the river is deep and dangerous in places, and the bed is littered with huge rocks. It was a terrible night, with rain, wind and darkness and it seems she managed to persuade the cow to cross the ravine. The pony, however, refused and would not budge. As the poor woman, with tears in her eyes, pleaded with and tempted the frightened pony, the Devil appeared to her.

She gasped out her story when Old Nick said, 'Fear not. I will build a bridge for you; it will be there in the morning – provided you agree to one condition.'

When she asked about the condition, Old Nick said that the price of the bridge was the soul of the first living thing that crossed it. The woman readily agreed and, leaving the cow to graze in the darkness, she returned to her home until the morning. And there, in the morning light, was the splendid, graceful, three-arched bridge which we can see today.

In building it, the Devil did not have an easy time. The wind was so strong, the night so dark and stormy that when he fetched the stones from the fells, some fell from his huge apron and littered the surrounding hillsides and river-bed.

Scattered around the area today are lots of large stones known variously as Devil's Neck-Collar on Casterton Fell, or the Apron-full-of-stones which is near Kingsdale.

However, the bridge itself was beautiful and when the lady arrived next morning, this time accompanied by her little dog, she was astonished. Now she could cross in comfort and safety with her dog and pony, for waiting at the other side was her precious cow. But the Devil was also waiting. 'There is your bridge as promised,' he said with evident pride. 'Now you must be the first to cross; your cow awaits and I will claim your soul as you agreed.'

'No, kind sir,' she said. 'You asked for the soul of the first living thing to cross the bridge, not *my* soul,' and in a trice she pulled a small bun from her apron pocket. In one throw, she hurled it across the bridge and called to her little dog, 'Fetch.'

The dog ran across the brige to retrieve the bun, thus being the first living thing to cross it, and so the Devil was cheated. He could have had the soul of a dog but he cheerfully admitted defeat. With a flash of his eyes and a cheeky grin, he disappeared from view, never to reappear. The crafty old lady continued her journey with a smile on her face. Her bridge remains to this day.

19   Kirksanton

The Underground Bells

Kirksanton is a small coastal village close to the southern tip of the Lake District in the Furness area. It is a couple of miles or so from Millom and stands on the A595 road which winds its way from Barrow-in-Furness along the Cumbria coast to Workington and eventually Carlisle.

Nearby Millom (with a population of 7,100), overlooking the sandy expanse of Duddon Sands, has little more to offer than its tiny neighbour. It is a small, exhausted industrial town of grey houses which has a rather run-down appearance, although it is surrounded by some picturesque countryside, much of it wooded. A former iron-ore producing community, its output reached a peak in the nineteenth century and it was producing some 300,000 tons annually by 1880. The decline began in the 1920s, although the ironworks were still operating in the 1960s.

In spite of its pervading air of depression, the town does incorporate a good deal of history including an ancient castle. It has a fine town hall overlooking a seedy market square below the church; Millom's beautiful old church, however, occupies a splendid hilltop site from where you can see snow-capped mountains, a row of modern windmills and some grey council estates. There was a sheep in the churchyard, perhaps working as the official grasscutter.

The red sandstone church with its graceful spire contains the tomb of John Huddleston, a member of a local family who were lords of the manor and whose coat of arms is carved on the fifteenth-century font. It was John Huddleston who administered the last sacrament to the dying King Charles II and one of the rights of the Huddlestons was to execute criminals on Gallows Field. A stone, known as the Hangstone, records this in the following inscription:

On this spot stood a gallows, the ancient
Lords of Millom having exercised
Jura regalia within their Seignory.

Jura regalia is the term meaning they had the power over life and death and they could authorize executions at this place. For another tale of the Huddleston family, see the section under Muncaster.

But we are not too concerned about the sadness of Millom. Kirksanton, a short distance to the north-west, is the focus of an old story which probably dates long before the time of the Huddlestons.

According to the legend, there used to be a church in Kirksanton many hundreds of years ago, the name 'kirk' meaning church. Then, quite unexpectedly, the ground around it opened up and a huge hole appeared. The church and its entire surroundings sank into the massive opening and the earth then closed over the top. Church and grounds vanished as if they had never existed (see also Kirkby Lonsdale).

It is said that the site can still be seen in the form of a depression in the ground. I did find such a hollow immediately on the left as one enters the village from Millom; it was serving as the village green and contained the beginnings of a 5 November bonfire.

It is said that if you approach this hollow on a Sunday morning and kneel so that your ear is close to the ground, it is still possible to hear the church bells ringing. These are the distant bells of Kirksanton's long-lost church.

20   Levens

The Luck of Levens Hall

This is one of several stories of lucks in the Lake District, the others being at Eden Hall, Great Salkeld and Muncaster (see the appropriate chapters). This differs from the others in that the so-called luck is not an ornamental object; instead, it is linked to a herd of deer.

Levens is a small hillside village some five miles south of Kendal. It comprises a host of neat grey houses a short distance from the junction of the A6 with the A590. With two busy main roads so close, Levens has managed to retain much of its solitude as it overlooks the distant lakeland hills.

Other than Sizergh Castle which is nearby, and the splendid Levens Hall which is the focus of our story but which stands apart from the village, there are few points of interest. The small grey church with its elegant spire and wide views, is dedicated to St John the Evangelist and was built in 1828. Its white-washed interior is very crisp, clean and light and, other than the east window behind the altar, none is fully made of stained glass. Two side windows near the altar do contain portions of stained glass, however, but the clear windows do give the church a very open and light appearance.

One curiosity can be found outside, at the rear of the west end of the church. Here is a small slate-roofed cote in which are hanging three large bells. For some unknown reason, these was brought from Milnthorpe in 1913 and installed at Levens – but the bells have no clappers and so they do not disturb the village. Another addition in 1913 was the fine lychgate and it was in the same year that burials were first carried out in this churchyard.

Levens Hall is some distance away with its entrance directly from the busy A6 while at the other side of that road is Levens Deer Park. This is the oldest deer park in England. There is a public footpath in the park and fishing permits can also be obtained.

Levens Hall stands in superb grounds to the south of the A590 and it is open to the public during the summer. It is an Elizabethan mansion built around 1580 but it has a central peel tower dating to the fourteenth century and one portion of the house can be traced to 1188. Its first builders were called Redman and they bought it from Ketel, the Baron of Kendal. By 1415, Richard Redman was Speaker of the House of Commons and it was probably a member of the Redman family who erected the famous peel tower.

The coat of arms of the Redmans, formerly known as Redmain or Redmayne, contained the odd symbols of three pillows. This arose from a duel which had to be fought by an early Redmayne. He arrived at the appointed place a long time before he was due to fight and instead of waiting, crept into a nearby tent and fell asleep. He slept so soundly that he did not hear the arrival of his foe, only becoming aware of his presence when the trumpets blew to announce the start of the contest.

Our Redmayne hero lost not a moment, however, because he leapt from his sleeping position, grabbed a sword and rushed out to meet his adversary. His swift action took everyone by surprise and he managed to defeat his opponent without too much trouble. Ever since, the story has been commemorated by placing three pillows in the family crest, a reminder of that sleepy ancestor!

Once a fortified home, Levens Hall is now a fine mansion and private family home which contains a wealth of treasures, some belonging to leaders like Nelson, Napoleon and Wellington. There are fine paintings, furnishings and some exquisite plaster work and chimney pieces. Oak panelling in the drawing-room dates to 1595 while the brightly coloured Spanish leather in the dining-room (*c.*1586) has given it the name of 'gilded parlour'.

Outside, there is a collection of steam engines while the gardens are noted throughout England and even overseas for their splendid topiary. This is the work of Monsieur Guillaume Beaumont who was the King's gardener in 1692; he also laid out the grounds of Hampton Court for James II and his work survives at Levens almost exactly as he designed it. It comprises carefully cut and designed examples of clipped and trimmed hedges, trees and shrubs in beech, box and yew.

But it is the deer park which provides the folk story known as the Luck of Leven Hall. In the surrounding district, it is believed that whenever a white fawn is born to the herd of dark fallow deer in the park, it heralds some event of importance to the Bagot family, the present owners of Levens Hall.

Some examples of this include a visit to the Hall by Lord Templetown after the Crimean War; General Upton's death in 1883; Captain and Mrs Bagot's wedding in 1885, when a white fawn was born the following day, and in 1896, when Mrs Bagot gave birth to a male heir. Following this belief, it is considered unlucky to harm or kill any of the white deer. An old example of this tells of the time when Lord Templetown, then owner of Levens Hall, ordered his gamekeeper to shoot a white buck which he had seen in the park.

Knowing the ancient legend, the gamekeeper was shocked by this instruction which he regarded as being worse than the crime of sacrilege, and so he went to remonstrate with his Lordship. But his master refused to believe such superstitious nonsense and repeated his order to kill the white buck.

The determined gamekeeper refused to obey and so the task was given to another man. But the buck's death was followed by all manner of disasters to the family and house.

Levens Hall twice changed hands, all the staff had their employment terminated while the family and the household suffered other torments and ill fortune. Local belief claimed this was all due to the shooting of the white buck.

There is an addition to this legend, however, which

involves a ghost called The Grey Lady. It is said to be the ghost of a gipsy who called at Levens Hall in the early part of the eighteenth century. She was seeking food and accommodation but was refused both and later died of starvation. Before her death, she laid a curse on Levens Hall and its occupants, saying that there would not be a son to inherit the hall until the year the River Kent ceased to flow and a white fawn was born to the herd in the Deer Park. And then, in 1896, Mrs Bagot gave birth to a son, Alan, and in the same year a hind produced a white fawn and the River Kent froze solid!

The Grey Lady has been seen several times since, sometimes by motorists on the A6 when she is accompanied by a small black dog.

21   Little Salkeld

The Story of Long Meg

There are two Salkelds, Great and Little. Great Salkeld is to the west of the River Eden, some seven miles north-east of Penrith, while Little Salkeld is at the other side of the river. It is a short distance from the A686 which leads from Penrith to Alston. Great Salkeld has two folk tales (see Great Salkeld), but its near neighbour can also boast an ancient story.

Little Salkeld has several places of interest – an eighteenth-century corn mill in red sandstone stands beside the beck which flows into the River Eden and it is now in working order, producing flour in the time-honoured way. There is a tea room too and an opportunity to inspect an exhibition about the old mill's methods of operation.

The seventeenth-century hall was virtually rebuilt little more than a hundred years or so after its construction. There is a tiny chapel with a small wooden porch and a bell on an iron stand above the roof. About a mile to the north of Little Salkeld is a series of natural cavities which appear to have been shaped over the centuries from a red sandstone cliff by the waters of the River Eden. These are known as Lacy's Caves. It seems, however, they were not made by nature.

A Colonel Lacy used to live in Salkeld Hall and in the eighteenth century, he ordered the excavation of these caves as a type of folly. They are splendidly made with arched doorways and the Colonel even paid a hermit to live in the caves, just to give them an air of ancient authenticity!

Of major interest here, however, is the ancient and remarkable stone circle known as Long Meg and Her Daughters. This is situated on a lofty hill about a mile from the village along a very narrow lane, and it is said to be the largest such circle in England, except for Stonehenge. It is also regarded as one of the most important archaeological sites in the country.

The circle is about 100 yards in diameter and is thought to date to 1500 BC, perhaps being the work of Bronze Age man (see also Keswick – the Castle Rigg Stone Circle). One odd fact is that the public road runs right through the middle of the circle, and sheep are grazing among the huge stones, for the circle is positioned on working farmland. One of the myths is that when you try to count the stones, the number varies every time! Reference books state that this family consists of around sixty stones. Precise figures are rarely given because no one seems able to make an accurate count. The number varies between fifty-nine and seventy-seven (I got to sixty-two!) but many of them conform to no particular shape, although some are taller than the average person. Others are some twelve foot or more around their girth and some are level with the ground. Perhaps some have now been covered by the earth, thus causing discrepancies in the numbers over the years. It is said, of course, that the stones possess some magic power which prevents anyone from counting the same number twice. Even the constituent rocks vary – some are made from granite, others from sandstone and some of limestone.

Of all the rocks, one stands out in particular and this is Long Meg. She is some twelve foot tall and stands erect and apart from the others, albeit leaning at a very slight angle. She tapers towards the top and stands alone, apparently being watched by four of her 'daughters' who form a kind of gateway.

Meg is said to be either a former witch, seductress, dancing girl or earth mother, but in one account she is supposed to be named after a boisterous lady of the court of King Henry VIII. She bears the curious 'Cup and Ring' markings which are to be found on other standing stones, some at Ilkley Moor in Yorkshire. Cup and ring markings consist of shallow hollows which have been carved from the rocks; they resemble the bottom halves of cups and are sometimes surrounded by a ring which is also carved in the rock, hence their name.

Wordsworth came to see this curious family in 1821. He called them 'that family forlorn'. He told how he had known of Long Meg since childhood but had never seen her until that moment, when the sight was sudden and unexpected. He said Meg was eighteen foot tall and felt that this was our most noble relic, except for Stonehenge.

How the stones got here is a mystery and so is their purpose, although there might be links with the Castle Rigg Stone Circle (see Keswick) and with a smaller circle about half a mile to the north-east of Long Meg. This is called Little Meg and comprises eleven stones.

As one might expect, several stories are associated with Long Meg and Her Daughters. One of the most curious is that if anyone breaks a piece off Long Meg, she will bleed and the story is that the surrounding stones are all her lovers who were turned to stone for reasons we do not know.

A similar tale says that Meg and her daughters were in fact a coven of witches who came to this magical place to perform their rituals. A local saint took exception to their bawdy, sacrilegious dancing and uttered a powerful prayer which promptly turned them all to stone.

The legend of their magic powers is attributed to a magician called Michael Scott. According to ancient memory, he endowed the stones with magical powers which meant they could never be counted accurately. Each time anyone counted them, the number would vary but if anyone did succeed in counting the same number twice, then the magical quality of the stones would come to an end. It seems that has never happened.

One story concerns an attempt to uproot the stones. Apparently Colonel Lacy, mentioned earlier in references to his caves, decided to remove the stones by explosives. As the preparations were being made, a fearsome thunderstorm broke out. The lightning was of a ferocity never before experienced in the vicinity and the wrath of the storm was such that the workmen ran for their lives.

The proposed blasting never took place and so the stones remain.

Even now, the stones do seem to exert some deep kind of magic or mystery; Meg and her daughters are just as puzzling as ever. If you don't believe this, just try to count them.

22   Muncaster

The Luck of Muncaster

The Luck of Muncaster is one of four lucks in the Lake District. The best known is perhaps the Luck of Eden Hall (see Edenhall), another is the Luck of Burrel Green (see Great Salkeld) while yet another is the Luck of Levens Hall (see Leven). The latter is of a different nature, being associated with a herd of deer while the others are all types of ornament.

Muncaster is near the foot of Eskdale on the coastal border of the Lake District and the region affords some excellent views of the central mountains and fells in addition to a fine expanse of the Irish Sea. It is about one mile from Ravenglass along the A595 and the entrance to the castle is on this road. John Ruskin, the Lakeland writer, described this entrance as 'Heaven's Gate', giving some indication of the splendours which lie behind.

Muncaster Castle has been the home of the Pennington family for almost 700 years; the castle is still owned by the family, the present occupant being Mr Patrick Gordon-Duff-Pennington. Pennington memorials in the church date to 1301 and one records the leadership of Sir John Pennington at the Battle of Flodden Field in 1513. There are further family memorials dating into this century, thus providing evidence of this enduring dynasty.

The castle is a splendid building which dates from the thirteenth century. Extended and enlarged several times from the original peel tower which stood on Roman foundations, it is sited in an extensive deer park which slopes to the banks of the River Esk. The grounds contain the fourth largest heronry in England, the famous Owl Centre, a world-renowned collection of azaleas and rhododendrons in addition to a nature trail and adventure playground.

There is also a sanctuary for rare birds and some exotic animals like wallabys and bears, while nearby are some Roman ruins called Clanaventa or Walls Castle. It is thought this once served as the baths for a Roman fort.

Indoors, the castle contains many treasures including fine paintings, furniture, books and tapestries. One famous painting depicts a man called Thomas Skelton. He is dressed in a long robe bearing squares and carries a staff on one hand and his hat in the other. His face has the look of a simpleton which is not surprising because he was known as The Fool of Muncaster. Although he was somewhat peculiar and rather dimwitted, he was employed as a jester at the castle.

It was in this role that he found himself involved in a terrible conflict. Sir Alan Pennington had a daughter called Helwise and she was engaged to marry Sir Ferdinand Huddleston of Millom Castle (see Kirkstanton). Secretly, however, she was in love with a handsome youth called Richard, the son of the village carpenter and they had arranged to meet on May Day.

The occasion was a May Day ceremony with maypole dancing, feasting and singing and it was to take place on the shores of nearby Devoke Water. Helwise tried to disguise herself by dressing as a humble shepherdess as she went to meet her lover but she attracted the unwelcome attentions of a ruffian called Wild Will of Whitbeck.

As Wild Will demanded a dance with Helwise, not knowing her true identity, Richard came to her rescue. Those who witnessed this moment recognized the light of love in their eyes. But Wild Will did not. He was angry and jealous; he saw no reason why the lovely maiden should prefer the handsome Richard and became determined to find out who she was. He followed the couple as they left the dancing and his trail took him to Muncaster Castle. There he saw them kissing at a side gate and realized who she was. He also knew that she was betrothed to Sir

Ferdinand Huddleston of Millom and decided to seek his revenge by informing on Richard.

He informed Sir Ferdinand of the girl's deception, knowing that Richard could well be executed for loving the girl of a knight of the realm. At the news, Sir Ferdinand flew into a violent rage; he was mortified that he had been made to look a fool by the son of a carpenter and decided to gain his own revenge. He managed to persuade the Muncaster jester, Thomas Skelton, to cut off the carpenter's head with an axe. For the task, he would be paid three crowns – and the fool agreed because he had also been deceived by Richard.

Tom Skelton stalked his prey and caught him in his wood shed where, with one swipe of the axe, he chopped off Richard's head and hid his body under the pile of wood shavings. The foolish actions of Tom Skelton have given rise to the word 'tomfoolery' but the scheming knight did not win his bride.

Sickened by the plotting, she went to live in a Benedictine Convent at Maiden Castle, spending the rest of her days in solitude and prayer. Sir Ferdinand joined the army and was killed in the Battle of Bosworth Field. He left his estate to St Mary's Abbey at Furness, with instructions that continuing Masses be said for the repose of his soul and that of the unfortunate Richard, a humble carpenter's son.

For all its legends and possessions, the most prized possession in the castle is the famous Muncaster Luck. This is a small, shallow and rather fragile bowl fashioned from green glass. It is about six inches in diameter and is decorated with gold and white enamel. So long as this bowl remains unbroken, the Pennington family will prosper – or so says the legend.

The story began in 1464 and involved King Henry VI. He was the only son of Henry of Agincourt and Catherine of France and he had been crowned king of England at the age of eight. He was also enthroned as King of France when he was ten. He grew into a studious, pious and caring person but was never a man of action.

Known as Holy King Harry, he was far too weak to cope with the political upheavals of his era and by the time he reached his early forties, he had lost his throne to Edward IV and had been taken prisoner. He was often engaged in battle, usually on the losing side, and found himself once more defeated and captured at Hexham. He managed to escape and fled across the hills to the Lake District where he lived rough for about a year. Heavily disguised, Henry managed to survive in the wilderness around the boundaries of Lancashire and Yorkshire. It was during his wanderings over Muncaster Fell in 1464 that a shepherd found him. He was in a pitiful state but managed to convince the shepherd of his true identity. He was therefore taken to Muncaster Castle. It was then the home of Sir John Pennington and he gave shelter to Henry for as long as he wished. Henry stayed for nine days during which time he slept and ate well, then left to continue his uncertain life.

In gratitude to Sir John, Henry gave him a glass drinking bowl and said that it was given to the family with a prayer that they might prosper for as long as the glass remained unbroken. That glass remains unbroken to this day, and the family has undoubtedly prospered.

Hanging in the bedroom used by King Henry there is a painting of him kneeling before an altar with the glass bowl in his right hand, and in the library there is another painting, on a wood panel, which depicts him with the luck.

About a mile from the castle, along the road to High Eskholme which lies beneath Muncaster Fell, there is a stone monument which marks the place where the unfortunate, wandering king was found by the Muncaster shepherd. The story of Henry VI, a pious and charming man, is a sad one which attracted the attentions of Shakespeare.

We learn something of Henry's gentle personality as we are told that even as he was being murdered in May 1471, at the Tower of London, he asked God to forgive his own sins and pardon his executioner.

23 Natland

The Treacle Mines

Natland is one of the outposts of Lakeland, lying along very narrow lanes some two miles south of Kendal. Passing places are provided – we had to use one to overtake a pedal cyclist! The village stands on an elevated plateau in a broad, green valley with the main Glasgow-London railway line running to the east and the River Kent to the west. Less than a mile away is Oxenholme Station where a branch line diverts to Windermere.

Natland itself is a very neat and tidy place; it is surprisingly pretty with its white and grey cottages and is a worthy winner of a county 'Best Kept Village' competition. There is a cluster of modern houses mixed with lovely old cottages around an historic and well-tended green and, although the village has spread due to the arrival of incomers, it does retain much of its olde-worlde character.

The green, whose records date to the thirteenth century, is overlooked by a mellow stone church which is astonishingly handsome. In spite of its medieval and historic appearance, it was built as recently as 1910 on the site of three earlier churches. Dedicated to St Mark, it boasts some splendid stained glass windows, an evergreen arch which serves as a lychgate and conveys an overall feeling of warmth and friendliness.

Few Lakeland villages boast a green of the type found in Natland, but in bygone times it was used as a gathering point for travellers such as gypsies, fairground people and itinerant traders. Today, there are seats for visitors.

The history of the village, however, dates to Roman times. The Romans had two camps nearby, one being a look-out post on Helm Hill; this occupied the site of a former Iron Age fort. The other Roman camp was called Alavna and is set in a loop of the River Kent midway between Natland and Kendal. This was almost certainly used by Agricola's army in AD 79 when he was heading for Scotland and increasing his grip on the north of England. The site of the camp is now known as the Watercrook. A fine old house on the site, also called Watercrook, is L-shaped and has a wing dating to the sixteenth century with two staircases, each about 350 years old.

Excavations on the Alavna/Watercrook site have produced many treasures which are now in the British Museum, including inscribed gravestones and an altar. One gravestone is of particular interest because the wording, which honours a soldier of the 20th Legion, adds a note of warning – it says that anyone placing another body in his grave will be fined!

There are some older buildings around the village. Natland Hall Farm, for example, has a seventeenth-century staircase while Natland Abbey, dating from the sixteenth century, was constructed like a letter H. Its doors and staircase are from the seventeenth century.

Another seventeenth century house is called High House and it has a wealth of period panelling and doors.

Overlooking Natland is an elongated hill called The Helm which is to the east of the A65. It is not particularly high, rising to just over 600 foot, but it does offer wide views from the summit. Just to the west of Natland is the Lancaster to Kendal canal which was opened in 1819, but the length between Kendal and Stainton, near Natland, has been closed and its channel filled in. The towpath remains as a public right-of-way and there is a canal bank nature trail.

Perhaps the most sought-after visitor attraction in Natland, however, is the treacle mine. The exact location is a very closely guarded secret and few people are permitted to visit this impressive place. Frequent attempts to break through the barrier of secrecy are made by people disguised as hikers, map-makers and treacle experts, but even today, the location is known to only a very few privileged people.

According to ancient legend, treacle was discovered centuries ago flowing in a cavern in Natland. It seems there is an unlimited underground reservoir which surfaces only at one particular place known as The Treacle Spring. The location of the treacle spring is perhaps Britain's best-known commercial secret; it has attracted the unwelcome attention of treacle mine saboteurs but to date, none has been able to penetrate the impressive security arrangements.

From the earliest times, treacle was used as an antidote against the bites of wild animals and other poisonous creatures although humans did find it useful for spreading on pancakes.

The name comes from the Latin *theriaca* and the Greek *theriake*, the prefix *ther* meaning wild beast. The people of ancient times used the name *treacle* to describe many antidotes against a variety of poisons and in time, the word became almost exclusively used to describe a compound of sixty-four drugs which were mixed with honey. The purest treacle was found in Venice and known as *theriaca andromachi* but the quality of the Natland product is superior. Indeed, it is perfect.

Sir Thomas More wrote about '*a most strong treacle against these venemous heresies*' and the Treacle Bible, otherwise known as the Bishop's Bible, published in 1568, contains in Jeremiah viii, 22 a quote, '*is there no tryacle in Gilead, is there no phisition there?*' In biblical times, tryacle was a word used to describe a balm and it appears in other places, eg Jeremiah xlvi, 11 and Ezekiel xxvii, 17.

The Treacle mines of Natland were discovered by accident in 1211 when a man was excavating for Roman treasures. He found a pot of the golden substance in a cave; it was being guarded by a venomous snake but the man believed the pot contained gold coins and decided to ignore the threat from the snake. As he made an effort to seize the crock, the snake sprang forward and bit him on the hand. The wound began to swell alarmingly and he fell to the floor in a semi-faint. As he fell, his injured hand crashed against the pot of golden fluid. It spilt on to the floor and when his hand dropped into it, it effected an instant cure.

As he recovered his health, he explored the cave and found the secret of the treacle mines – a small fissure in the cave had been sealed with a wooden plug and when he removed it, the treacle began to flow in a never-ending stream. He plugged the fissure and knew that he had, indeed, made his fortune. He had found a never-ending supply of treacle and from that day to this, the spring deep in the treacle mine is still producing gallons of the precious fluid.

Today, the only way to discover the whereabouts of the famous mine is to try and follow the ladies of Natland. Whenever Natland children become too inquisitive by asking awkward questions about any subject, their mothers will stop them by saying, 'I haven't time to answer your questions, I'm going to the treacle mine.'

When I arrived in the village in search of the mine, a lady told me, 'Oh, it's here all right! Whenever a man is late home from the pub, he always apologises by saying, "Sorry, I've been to the treacle mine!" '

Should anyone succeed in finding out where those mothers go, or where those gentlemen disappear to after a drink at the pub, they could discover Natland's best kept secret.

24   Penrith

A Giant's Grave
and the Hart's Horn Tree

Half a dozen main roads converge on Penrith in addition to the main London–Glasgow railway line and the M6 motorway. In many ways, therefore, it is the gateway to the Lake District and yet, with a population of just over 13,500, it remains a fairly modest if busy market town. In the ninth and tenth centuries, however, it was the capital of Cumbria, Cumbria then being a semi-independent state and part of Strathclyde in the Kingdom of Scotland.

Today, there are some delightful Lakeland-style buildings and cottages, many constructed in the local red sandstone, and they mingle prettily with an assortment of Elizabethan buildings, modern shops and offices. The town boasts a market charter which dates to 1223; that market continues to draw traders and buyers from a wide area, serving farmsteads and country people from the surrounding villages. To the west of the market square is the Cornmarket which has open stalls on market day (Tuesday), while there is an out-of-town auction mart on Thursdays. On the road from the Cornmarket to the castle is the Penrith Steam Museum which contains traction engines, organs, a working blacksmith's shop and other displays.

A good walk from Penrith takes you to the tree-covered Penrith Beacon which rises to almost 1,000 feet and from where there are splendid views, particularly of Ullswater. The first so-called pike or tower on the top was used in the middle ages, around 1296, but the present structure was built in 1719. For centuries, this vantage point has served as a look-out position because it was the ideal place from which to send warnings by fire to neighbouring beacons.

The Beacon used to be the site of Penrith's gibbet. It was used in 1767 to display the remains of a murderer called Thomas Nicholas. Nicholas was hanged at Carlisle on 31 August 1767 and his body suspended in chains from the Penrith Beacon gibbet. On 18 November 1766, he had killed a man called Thomas Parker who was a butcher from Langwathby and the crime was committed in an old quarry on the slopes of this beacon. A mystery occurred before the execution because the letters T.P.M. were cut into the turf on the slopes of the hill. Some thought these were the initials of the true killer, Nicholas being wrongly accused. It seems, however, that they might have stood for Thomas Parker – Murdered. Another theory is that the letter P was a badly shaped attempt to depict the gallows and that the M should have been an N, the initials thus being T.N. and so referring to Thomas Nicholson's forthcoming execution. Even so, no one is quite sure what the letters meant, or who carved them into the hillside turf.

Wordsworth, as a child, came riding this way with a friend and they got separated. As young Wordsworth approached the gallows site he realized there was a body hanging in chains and later, he was to comment on the Nicholson hanging. One of his lines says, 'Some unknown man had carved the murderer's name' so perhaps the letters were the initials of Thomas Nicholson with a crudely drawn gallows between.

For a time, Penrith lay within the Kingdom of Scotland and it was recovered for England by Edward I (1239–1307) but its first castle did not appear until 1399. It was constructed after Penrith had been burnt to the ground by Scottish raiders in 1345. The castle was the work of a man called William Strickland. He was rector of Horncastle and later became Bishop of Carlisle, eventually becoming Archbiship of Canterbury. He was a noted benefactor to the town.

Today, there are scant remains of his castle; later parts were added by Ralph Neville and Richard of Gloucester.

One of its occupants was Richard, Earl of Warwick known as Warwick the Kingmaker; Gloucester, when he became King Richard III, also lived here for a time. In spite of its history, the ruin is not very spectacular, comprising little more than a south wall. It stands not far from the railway station and is open to the public.

Richard of Gloucester is said to have stayed in Penrith at one of the local inns, the Gloucester Arms, before he became King Richard III.

This old inn can be seen in a large market-place known as Great Dockray; it is opposite the oddly named Board and Elbow inn and there are two white boars over the entrance which are reminders of King Richard's visit. The boar was part of his coat of arms. Bonnie Prince Charlie came to Penrith too, and lodged at the George Hotel in the market-place during the rebellion of 1745. William Wordsworth was educated at Penrith in Dame Birkett's School along with his sister, Dorothy. He was seven and she was six. A Tudor house near the church bears the initials and date RB 1663 and this was that old school. Wordsworth met his future wife here too, Mary Hutchinson. Later she went to live at Brompton, near Scarborough in North Yorkshire where, on 4 October 1802, Wordsworth married her. Wordsworth's mother and Mary's parents are all buried in Penrith churchyard, although the whereabouts of Mrs Wordsworth's grave is unknown. Mrs Wordsworth died when her son was only eight and was never aware of his massive achievements.

Parts of the parish church of St Andrew date to the eighteenth century, being rebuilt in 1772, and in some respects it looks more like a church hall than an actual church. Its interior is large and rather unusual too, although some portions of the defensive clock tower have survived since the thirteenth century. Here, the red sandstone shows signs of wear and inside there are some Tudor relics, ancient fonts and interesting memorials with shields and lettering.

There was probably a Saxon church on this site too. The pillars which support the panelled gallery are also worth a second glance – each is created from a single piece of stone ten foot tall and some four foot in circumference.

One memorial commemorates a plague in Elizabethan times which killed 2,260 local people, and in a field on the road to Kendal there is a square plague-stone, rather like a huge font, in which the people of Penrith washed their money, probably in vinegar, in an attempt to de-contaminate it. They also stopped here, well outside the plague-ridden town, to exchange their market wares and produce.

From a legendary point of view, the churchyard contains some very old items. One is a pre-Norman cross known as the Giant's Thumb, but more important is the Giant's Grave. This has been here for more than a thousand years and is said to be the grave of Owen or Ewan Caesarius who was King of Cumbria from AD 920 to AD 937. He was a man of gigantic proportions and there is a suggestion that he is the Grim Baron of Castle Hewin (See Hesket-in-the-Forest). The castle in that village might have been called Castle Ewan in honour of the giant, and not Castle Hewin as it later became known.

The Giant's Grave is readily identified by two shafts of former crosses each some ten foot tall which stand fifteen foot apart. These mark the head and foot of the Giant's Grave. Four hogback stones lie between the uprights. These have the appearances of miniature houses with carvings on the sloping roofs. In the past, these distinctive stones were used as coverings for graves. Some time between 1582 and 1590, the grave was opened by someone called Turner and it was said that the bones of a huge man were found there. One slight variation of name says the grave might be that of Ewan Caesario who lived in the fifth century and who was not therefore a king of the tenth century. This Ewan was known as a slayer of bears and robbers! Caesario or Caesarius is just one of several legendary giants who lived in the Lake District. There used to be another at Eamont Bridge on the A6 just outside Penrith where there were series of giants' caves.

According to legend, the caves were the haunt of a giant called Isir who caught and ate both human and animal prey. He devoured them in those caves, although in reality, the caves might be nothing more than shelters used by primitive people. This would explain the presence of any bones found there.

Nonetheless, the caves were the scene of an annual festival which died out during the last century. It was known as Giant's Cave Sunday. It was still being observed in 1850 but has since vanished from our calendar; all that remains is an account which says that the children carried 'shaking bottles' during the ceremony, but no one seems to know what these were.

Some years after the legendary Isir lived in this cave, it became the home of a hermit-monk, probably in the fifteenth century, but there is little information about his presence and work. The monk, however, may have had some influence on the building of a new bridge at Eamont in 1425 because upon the bridge there was a cross with steps and seats around it. Before the Reformation, mass was often said at such crosses and the seats may have been provided for the congregation. Another link with the church was that the Bishop of Durham granted an indulgence of forty days to everyone who truly repented of their sins and who contributed any goods for the building of 'a new bridge over the River Anot in the parish of Penrith'. That river is now called the Eamont and flows from Ullswater into the River Eden.

Close to where the B5320 joins the A6 at Eamont Bridge, there are further links with King Arthur and his Knights of the Round Table. At this location is a place known as King Arthur's Round Table. Legend says this is where the famous Arthur met with his equally famous Knights (see also Carlisle), but the relic is probably a Bronze Age burial mound dating from 1800 BC. Nearby are further Neolithic remains known as the Mayburgh Monument. Dating from 2000 BC, this used to consist of two concentric circles of standing stones, with two pairs flanking the entrance. Now, only one stone remains. It is some fifteen feet tall and the entire complex, when complete, is thought to have been used for ancient religious ceremonies.

Penrith's surviving folk story concerns the Hart's Horn Tree which disappeared long ago. This tale involves an area known as Whinfell Forest some four miles to the east of Penrith along the A66 road towards Appleby. Centuries ago, the forest contained a splendid oak tree which became known as the Hart's Horn Tree and the reason for this name dates to the fourteenth century.

In 1333, Edward Baliol, the King of Scotland, entered Westmorland to visit Lord Robert de Clifford at several of Clifford's castles. They included Appleby, Brougham and Pendragon and it was while staying at Brougham Castle near Penrith that the royal party went stag hunting. During the chase, they put up a splendid stag which fled from Whinfell Forest towards the Scottish border, which was then much closer than it is now. The stag outran all the dogs except a solitary greyhound called Hercules. When the stag grew close to the Scottish border, it suddenly turned back towards Whinfell. As the exhausted stag, followed by the equally exhausted greyhound, approached the safety of Whinfell Forest, the stag made a tremendous leap for freedom.

It leapt over some palings but that final effort was too much; it collapsed and died immediately upon clearing the fence. Hercules the greyhound tried to execute the same leap but he dropped dead at the near side of the palings. Thus hunter and hunted lay dead, their bodies separated by the palings.

The courage of the stag and the tenacity of the greyhound impressed Lord de Clifford so much that he created a memorial to both animals. He removed the stag's fine head of antlers and nailed them to a nearby oak tree, saying that Hercules had killed a stag, but the stag had also killed Hercules.

As the years passed, the oak grew larger and in time the antlers became grafted to the wood. Eventually, it looked as if the antlers were sprouting from the oak. Oak trees are very long-lived and three hundred years later, the Hart's Horn Tree was still standing in Whinfell Forest. It was known to be there in 1648 with the stag's horns still protruding.

Sadly, it was damaged by a passing Parliamentary soldier and then in 1658, some vandals of the period went into the forest at night and stole the antlers. They were never recovered. By this time, the old oak was past its best and parts were decaying but even then, more than three hundred years after the death of two gallant animals, the

Hart's Horn Tree continued to be a point of interest. People would walk into the forest to examine it and the nobility of the area would take their friends and visitors to see this curious hunting memorial.

25 Renwick

The Renwick Cockatrice

Renwick lies on the far north-eastern boundary of the
Lake District close to the Northumberland border. About
ten miles from Penrith, it is on the wild slopes of Watch
Hill which towers 2,000 foot behind the village. Access is
via a network of narrow twisting and steep lanes, often
without signposts, from either the B6413 (Lazenby-
Kirkoswald-Brampton road) or the A686 (Penrith to Alston
road). Beyond Renwick are the Northumberland hills
which were snow-covered when I arrived in October, and
the valley of the South Tyne, with Gilderdale Forest
marking the road into Alston. The fells are remote, bleak
and deserted, a fact symbolized in the name of one of the
slopes – Fiends's Fell.

Renwick is a small, quiet village with an ornate red sandstone Methodist chapel; streams flow from the heights into
the River Eden in the valley below but in spite of its lonesome
appeal, visitors are few. As I entered the quiet churchyard,
the only sounds were of birds singing in the nearby trees,
and of a stream rippling just behind the church.

Nearby is the site of Haresceugh Castle, the only
remains of which, after some 650 years of history, are
small portions of stone walls.

The church of red sandstone with a blue slate roof is
dedicated to All Saints and affords some shelter to visitors.
It is a plain building bearing the date 1845 and its roof is on
two levels, each bearing a tiny cross on the ridge. There is
also a tiny belfry containing two bells, but this is not the
original building.

Until 1733, an older church occupied this site. It had in fact been rebuilt that year and boasted a fine double-decker pulpit and a bell which was more than 500 years old. In 1845, the church underwent further rebuilding and it was during one of these rebuilding sessions, almost certainly the earlier one, that a workman suffered a terrible fright. His experience has become known as the Renwick Bat or the Renwick Cockatrice.

While the higher parts of the pre-1733 church were being demolished by a workman, a fearsome black creature flew out of the rafters. On the ground below, several other workmen saw it and all were terrified. Some described it as a giant bat or a vampire while others said it was a crackachrist.

A crackachrist is an old local word for cockatrice which was a lowly species of dragon. Legend said that a cockatrice was a cross between a dragon and a bird – the creature was hatched by a dragon from a cock's egg! It was especially feared because it could kill at a glance and if local yarns are to be believed, much of rural England was once infested by these terrifying creatures.

Tales of their flights around the remote villages were such that there were times when the villagers dare not leave their homes. In the stories, however, the end of the terror came when a gallant knight clad himself in shining mirrors and walked around the known haunts of the cockatrices. As each creature saw its own reflection in the mirror, it died instantly from its own death-delivering glance. Word of this success soon spread and with such a foolproof anti-cockatrice weapon as a simple mirror, it is not surprising that they soon became extinct.

Memories of them still linger. In Wherwell, a village in Hampshire, a cockatrice was said to fly around Wherwell Priory before its dissolution in 1538. A reward of four acres of land was offered to anyone who could kill it and eventually a man called Green volunteered. He discovered the creature's lair and lowered a mirror into it. The cockatrice glared at its own reflection and died, and Mr Green was rewarded with his gift of land. In Harewood Forest, near Wherwell, there is still a plot of land known as Green's Acre and in Andover Museum there is the winged figure of the cockatrice which once sat upon the weather-vane of Wherwell Church. It has a long pointed tail, two claw-like front legs and a fearsome curved beak.

There is little wonder, therefore, that the workmen at Renwick Church ran for their lives when they feared that such a creature had materialized from the ruins. One of them, however, far braver than the others, decided to tackle the creature. He was called John Tallantire and he reckoned it was nothing more than a large bat. Even so, he was just a little superstitious and, knowing the ancient lore regarding witches and other evil things, armed himself with a thick branch taken from a rowan tree. He thought it was more useful than a mirror! The rowan is also known as the mountain ash and its timber has always been regarded as ideal for warding off evil spirits and witches. Thus armed, our Renwick saviour commenced battle with the creature.

The precise details of John Tallantire's brave fight do not survive, but we do know that he positively defeated the fearsome thing, whatever it was. From that moment, he became a local hero and like Mr Green from Wherwell, was duly rewarded. In this case he was made exempt from paying tithes for his property which was at the hamlet of Scale. Tithes were a form of tax which was paid to the church authorities.

And so the Renwick cockatrice or Renwick bat was removed from the scene and the villagers relaxed. From that time, the men of Renwick became known as Renwick Bats. Even now, visitors are few and the local people do say that if you walk on to the fells during the evening, you can still see a large, black bat-like creature flying around the village.

So, if you do decide to explore Renwick and district, perhaps it would be wise to carry a mirror!

26 Rottington

A Giant's Grave

Between Rottington and St Bees, there is said to be a giant's grave. This is just one of several legendary giants' graves in the Lake District.

Lying about four miles south of Whitehaven along narrow lanes, Rottington is a tiny coastal community of red sandstone farms and cottages only a mile or so from St Bees. With beautiful views, it is Cumbria's most westerly community.

The giant is variously known as the Rottington Giant or the Giant of St Bees. I shall regard him as belonging to the former because his name was Rottin and it is claimed he gave his name to that village.

The story begins in the time of the Vikings and the tale has distant links with the life of St Bee. Could this be a variation of her story? Her father wanted her to marry a handsome Viking prince but she refused and entered a convent after fleeing from the fellow (see St Bees).

This story begins when hordes of vicious Norsemen invaded Cumbria and landed on the shoreline near St Bees Head. Rottin was the leader of a particularly ferocious gang. He was a giant of a man who was noted for his bravery and his tough, handsome appearance. As well as being a noted raider, however, he was also a charmer and huge numbers of women were attracted to him. He took full advantage of their desire, making love to one and all, but being faithful to none. It is said that he left a trail of broken hearts wherever he went.

But Rottin had a wife called Inngunn. She was said to be

the most beautiful of women and she had accompanied him on one fateful trip. He had left her on the Isle of Mona, now called the Isle of Man, where she was almost a queen. Certainly, she was mistress of Mona for it was between 800 and 815 that the Vikings conquered the island, more Norsemen arriving between 850 and 990. Eventually, she became aware of Rottin's constant unfaithfulness and became increasingly unsettled by his life-style while he was away from her. Stories of his wild behaviour began to filter back to her and the result was that, over a long period, her love turned to distrust and finally hatred. When he embarked on his trip to Cumbria, therefore, she decided to follow him in secret.

Rottin and his band of maurauders beached near St Bees late one summer evening and the first place they discovered was the convent which had been founded some two centuries earlier by St Bega, also known as Bee. The abbess was called Hilda but she was not the famous St Hilda from Whitby – that Hilda had died in AD 680.

As the band of evil Vikings approached the silent church, Hilda was kneeling before the altar in deep prayer. The church door was open and the entire complex was unguarded – hitherto it had not been considered necessary to guard either the church or the nuns. Hilda was so engrossed in her devotions that she was unaware of the men's presence and before she could retaliate or cry out, Rottin had crept behind her. He seized her with one huge arm and put his hand over her mouth to stop her from calling for help, then carried her off to his camp beyond the abbey. His men raided the convent, searching all the dormitories and cells for the other nuns and all were forced to join the Vikings at their camp. There they were repeatedly raped and attacked; they were made to act as servants, cooking meals and being forced to obey every order of this ruthless army. Their lovely church was demolished and its remains burnt to cinders. The gentle nuns, whose vows of chastity, poverty and obedience to God had been so viciously violated, were little more than prisoners. Whenever the Vikings went into the surrounding countryside on one of their plundering raids, guards were left to ensure the women never left the premises.

In spite of her treatment, Hilda never forgot the power of prayer and spent a lot of her free time, such as it was, kneeling on the shore and praying for deliverance. She asked God to spare the sisters from this monster and his men.

Then one day she was alone on the beach, the Vikings having embarked on another raiding foray into Cumberland. By now, her guard had relaxed, seeing little risk from a nun at prayer. As she raised her head from her prayers that day, Hilda noticed a small boat approaching the shore. It carried two women, one of whom was particularly beautiful and expensively attired. This was Inngunn, the mistress of Mona, and her companion was a slave. Hilda, now alone without the guard, went to meet them and help them ashore. As they talked in hushed tones, Inngunn was provided with a full account of the terrible deeds of the man she had grown to hate. Hilda confirmed everything that Inngunn had long suspected.

Despite her experiences, Hilda's attitude remained one of forgiveness; all she wanted was to leave this place and return to her life of peace and tranquillity in a convent. The revengeful Inngunn had other ideas, however. She wanted revenge and was determined to repay Rottin for his treachery.

Knowing of the nun's holy ideals, Inngunn made her plans in secret and after a few days living in hiding nearby, she again contacted Hilda. This time, she carried a small casket.

Around this time, the band of Vikings had returned from their raids and were exhausted, but happy. It had been a good trip and they were in the mood for love and relaxation. The unfortunate nuns were called upon to satisfy all their lusts and afterwards, were told to prepare the food and drink for a party. A superb spread of food and wine was prepared.

Inngunn had chosen her time well and now sought Hilda, making sure she was never seen by her husband and his men. She asked Hilda to pour the contents of a small phial into Rottin's drink as she prepared it. Inngunn produced the phial from her casket and told Hilda it was a love potion, the purpose being to entice Rottin to renew his love for her. Innocently, Hilda obeyed. As she prepared the goblet of finest wine for Rottin, she poured in the contents of the phial. Soon, the entire band of Vikings were singing and making merry, then Rottin demanded that Hilda accompany him to his chamber. As before, she obeyed even though she was unwilling, but hardly had Rottin climbed into his bed of animal skins than he fell into a deep slumber. Thankfully, Hilda left him but Inngunn was hiding in the passage. As the quiet nun vanished along the corridor, Inngunn crept in and spoke to her husband. He recognized her voice; puzzled, he tried to sit up and protect himself for he guessed her intentions, but the drug was too powerful and he slumped into bed. Inngunn, in her final act of revenge, plunged a dagger into his black heart, stabbing him time and time again.

She left as quietly as she had come, taking her tiny boat back to Mona and leaving the body for Rottin's servants to discover in the morning. And so Rottin, the huge, evil giant, died violent death. He was buried in a massive grave not far from the ruined convent. Today, his place of burial is still known as the Giant's Grave, and the village is called Rottington.

27   St Bees

A Summer Snowfall

St Bees is an ancient but pretty coastal village of grey-roofed houses set on the west-facing slopes of a valley some five miles south of Whitehaven. With a long main street descending into the centre, it is said to be the nicest place from which to set out upon a trip to Ennerdale Water.

To the north west, St Bees Head juts into the waters of the Irish Sea. The promontory with its pinkish coloured rocks has for centuries served to warn shipping of dangers along this coastline. A lighthouse stands high on the cliffs to continue this work but in spite of its presence, the centuries have witnessed many dramas and shipwrecks off this coast.

In the village, the church is believed to be the oldest in west Cumbria, the first being founded by St Bega some time around AD 650. Nothing of that early church has survived, probably being destroyed by the invading Danes (see Rottington) and a second building was started around 1125. It was constructed under the auspices of the wealthy St Mary's Abbey of York, and the present beautiful church of red sandstone, albeit no longer Catholic stands on the site. It is a massive church, far too large for the village, but this gives some indication of its past importance for, before the Reformation, it was a priory serving a community of monks.

With a splendid ornate doorway, the church contains some ancient relics, such as a piscina and a stoup from the twelfth century while the churchyard also contains a wealth of monuments as well as an old cross. Other old buildings in St Bees include a bridge, some charming houses and the famous public school of St Bees, one wing of which dates to the sixteenth century.

The church continues to spring surprises – as recently as 1981 some students were excavating to the south of the chancel where there was an aisle, added about 1300. This was ruinous before 1539, probably due to the ravages of the Reformation, but they found a sealed lead coffin. Inside was the shrouded body of a man whose flesh and organs were hardly decayed. Even his blood was fluid and it was thought to be that of a Crusader who had died around 1368. It was even discovered, through a post-mortem, that his last meal had included grapes.

According to one old folk tale, it was an incident in the seventh century that established a community of nuns here and gave St Bees its rather odd name. In its early days, it was called Kirby Beagogh, meaning the church and town of Bega. Some authorities, however, claim there was no such person as Bega, Begu or Bee, as her name is variously spelt. Some claim that the name comes from Sancta Bega which is a combination of Latin and Anglo-Saxon. It does not mean Saint Bega as it would seem, although sancta in Latin does mean holy but bega in Anglo-Saxon meant ring. Thus it would seem the words infer that there is, or was, a holy ring somehow involved and, in fact, there used to be a holy ring or bracelet in the church at St Bees. This remained until the thirteenth century and legend said the ring had been given to St Bega by an angel.

There is, however, good reason for believing that Bega was a real person because this was the name of a nun at Hackness in North Yorkshire. She founded a convent in the place now called St Bees. Although the story of the founding of St Bees involves a charming folk tale, it is just one of two accounts of the founding of that nunnery. The first story does have the authority of the Venerable Bede who recorded the incident in his *History of the English Church and People* (chapter 23 of Book IV).

It concerned the death of St Hilda, Whitby's famous abbess. The small community of nuns at Hackness was an offshoot of Whitby Abbey; situated sixteen miles away, it was founded in AD 680. In the final seven years of her life, St Hilda was a sick woman and on her last day, aged sixty-six, she seems to have known she was to die during the night. She attended mass, took Holy Communion and called the community around her, admonishing them to preserve peace among themselves and with all others.

Sixteen miles away at Hackness, a nun called Bega or Begu, who had served God for thirty years, was sleeping in the dormitory when she heard the sound of a bell. It was the sound that roused the community for prayers but when Bega opened her eyes, she saw that the roof of the convent appeared to be open and a glorious light shone through. Through the opening, and in the brilliant light, she saw the soul of Abbess Hilda being carried towards heaven, accompanied by a band of angels.

Terrified by what she had seen, Bega roused the senior nun, whose name was Frigyth and she summoned the entire community to prayer in the church. Later, the nuns learned that Hilda, sixteen miles away at Whitby, had in fact died that very hour; it was the 17 of November 680. Thus Bega had witnessed a unique event – a saint rising to heaven at the precise moment it happened. The account is of further interest because it mentions a bell, and this is thought to be the very first time that a bell is mentioned in ecclesiastical history.

Shortly afterwards Bega was transferred to a small village on the west coast of Cumberland, to establish another small monastery. That village and the monastery became known as St Bees.

The second tale also involves a nun or a saint known as Bega and dates to the seventh century. This Begu or Bega was an Irish nun of royal descent; some accounts say she was a princess but in spite of her privileged background, she decided to dedicate her life to God and good works.

This decision did not please her father who had plans for her to marry a Viking prince (for another tale of a Viking and a nun, see Rottington, a village close to St Bees). Fearing Bega might run away, he forbade her to leave the palace. She had to remain under guard until the wedding, but Bega had other ideas.

One night, there was a lively party at the palace with lots of guests and as the merrymaking grew more and more boisterous, Bega managed to dodge her guards and slip away into the darkness. No one missed her until morning but, in the meantime, she had managed to ride a fast horse into the countryside to gain the privacy of a distant convent. There she was protected as she prepared herself for the life of a nun. Her father, however did not give up. He launched a very detailed search of all the Irish convents and when Bega learned of his determination, she decided to flee even further. She would cross the sea to England and so she set off in a small boat, accompanied by a party of supportive nuns.

As the tiny craft approached the Cumbrian coast, however, a terrible storm blew up and it tossed the tiny boat around like a cork. The nuns prayed for their lives. They were all thrown into the sea, but, fortunately, they were fairly close to the beach and managed to scramble ashore. They had lost everything – they had no money, no belongings and no home. As they lay exhausted, soaked to the skin and very worried, Bega took command and said she was going to seek help.

She found her way to nearby Egremont (see Egremont) where she knew of the Lady of Egremont who lived in the fine castle. Bega's royal birth undoubtedly helped for she was given access to the Lady of Egremont. Following their conversation, Bega and her small band of nuns were admitted to the castle with a promise they could remain until they could find alternative accommodation. While they were enjoying this hospitality, it seems that Bega and Lady Egremont became firm friends.

It was this friendship, and perhaps the delightful countryside of the district, that convinced Bega that she should remain. She wanted to establish a nunnery here, but she had no land, no money and none of the qualities needed to build and maintain a church and a convent. All she had was faith.

She discussed her wishes with Lady Egremont who promised to have a word with her husband. He owned a huge amount of land, much of which was never used, and Lady Egremont felt sure he would donate a small parcel of it to the nuns. He might even be persuaded to give them help with the equipment and tools they would require to build their convent.

On midsummer's eve, therefore, the Lord of Egremont summoned Bega for a meeting to discuss her ideas and it seems he was not too keen to either donate the land or to provide the nuns with help and materials. He was good enough to listen, however, and being a kindly man, he did not wish to upset his wife as she was obviously keen to have the nuns living nearby. Jokingly, therefore, he said, 'Bega, I will give you as much land as is covered by snow tomorrow morning and I will support your enterprise with stones, wood and labour!'

And with that, he swept from the room, chuckling at his own guile. As the following day was Midsummer Day, the nuns and Lady Egremont felt a sense of dismay and went away sorrowing. Bega went to pray, however.

Next morning, the ground was covered with snow. For three miles around the castle, the entire landscape was white with a new fall of snow and Lord Egremont was astonished. But he was a man of his word and recalled Bega to say she could have the necessary piece of land and materials. He realized that a power far greater than he was supporting Bega and her party of nuns, and so building of the new convent commenced.

Bega became a famous, respected and much loved abbess who spent her life caring for the sick and helping the poor, and the area became known as St Bees in her honour.

28   Souther Fell

Everlasting Trout and a Spectral Army

Souther Fell is an imposing mountain and part of the block which includes Skiddaw and Saddleback, the latter being also known as Blencathra. Souther Fell is much smaller than either of these, rising only to some 1,680 foot. It is a formidable if unexciting climb which is rewarded at the summit by some splendid views, especially of the Pennines. The tops of the hills were dusted with snow as I arrived in October while their lower slopes were adorned in the superb colours of autumn.

There is one legend in this area, and one ghost story which has been elevated to the status of a folk tale.

The legend concerns a tarn which nestles in the folds of Bowscale Fell. This sombre mountain, 'at the back o' Skiddaw', overlooks Mungrisdale and can be approached only by foot. You take your car along narrow lanes through the rugged countryside to Mungrisdale and about one mile north, you come to the hamlet of Bowscale. Horses roam free upon this landscape, unfenced like the mountain sheep of Lakeland. A footpath leads along the fellside above the River Caldew and takes you to Bowscale Tarn, a tiny but pretty mountain lake.

According to legend, the tarn contains two massive trout which defy capture. They swim for ever in these cool, fresh waters and no one has been able to net them or hook them. They are immortal fish, so the story goes and Wordsworth described them as 'undying fish that swim in Bowscales Tarn'.

Little over a mile from Bowscale Tarn is the renowned

Souther Fell, scene of an amazing ghost story. It was once known as Souter Fell or Soutra Fell and lies just to the north of the A66 between Threlkeld (see Threlkeld) and Penruddock. It overlooks a new section of this road which was constructed near the hamlet of Scales in 1976.

Souther Fell would not feature prominently in books about the Lake District but for a startling series of events which began in 1735. This collection of folk stories does not purport to include many ghost stories, but the events on Souther Fell have become part of the traditional folklore of the Lake District. It concerns a ghostly army which was seen on several occasions by different people while it was marching across the summit of this mountain. Had there been just one sighting by a solitary person, not much heed would have been taken, but repeated sightings by different people at different times does add a wonderful air of mystique to the tale.

The story begins on midsummer's eve, 1735, when a man employed by a Mr William Lancaster of Blakehills, a hamlet near Mungrisdale, was walking on the eastern side of Souther Fell. Blakehills is about half a mile from the hamlet of Southerfell which is at the bottom of the slopes of the mountain.

Mr Lancaster's servant noticed movements on the top of the mountain and he saw that they consisted of an army on the march with distinct bodies of troops. He watched them for about an hour as they came from an eminence at the north end of the summit and marched over a niche in the top. The man told Mr Lancaster of his experience but because no one else had seen the soldiers, the witness was derided and people made fun of him.

Two years later to the very day, Mr Lancaster himself was walking on the fell. It was midsummer's eve, between eight and nine o'clock at night, and he heard what he thought were several horsemen. They seemed to be walking some distance behind their own horses, as if they had been hunting, and so he ignored them. Ten minutes later, he looked at them again and now saw they were mounted. This time, they had the appearance of a large army of cavalrymen riding in columns of five, and they were crowded upon the very same place that his servant had reported his sighting.

Mr Lancaster called his family and they came to examine the phenomenon. They all agreed with what he had seen – a large army of horsemen riding five abreast. From time to time, one of the five would leave the others. He would stand and watch the moving army, as if observing and regulating their movements, and would then gallop forward to resume his place. Figures regularly quitted the lines and these appeared to be coming from the middle ranks. It seemed as if they were marshalling the troops and keeping them in some kind of disciplined order.

In William Hutchinson's *The History of Cumberland* (1793) there is an account of Mr Lancaster's sighting in which he said, 'As it grew later, they seemed more regardless of discipline, and rather had the appearance of people riding from a market than an army, though they continued crowding on, and marching off, as long as there was light to see them.'

There were no further reported sightings of this ghostly army until midsummer's eve 1745, just before the Scotch rebellion of that year. When the army made its appearance on this occasion, Mr Lancaster and his family went out and drew the attention of their neighbours and friends. They had ridiculed the Lancasters on earlier occasions, but now some twenty-six people assembled on the side of Souther Fell to watch the army on the mountain top.

So real was the sighting that some of the observers actually climbed to the summit in the hope of finding evidence of a trick, such as a cast horseshoe, a footprint or some other object. But there was nothing, not even a footprint in the soft earth of the summit. Mr Lancaster made the point that he had never claimed they were real people. The natural features of the mountain, including some precipices, made it virtually impossible for such a large number of people and horses to congregate there and execute the movements he had witnessed.

He said, however, that the apparitions were not like clouds or vapour, they looked like real men on real horses, sometimes with carriages interspersed, and so large was the group of people that it extended for about half a mile.

He had watched the army for more than an hour as it marched across the summit of Souther Fell and it was only the onset of darkness that concealed them from his sight. Now, he was not afraid to tell anyone. In fact, he persuaded the twenty-six other witnesses to swear before a magistrate on oath as to what each had seen that evening. Every one of them swore they had seen the ghostly army on Souther Fell and all told an identical story.

There are many theories about this experience, one of which was that troops were in fact exercising on the eve of the 1745 rebellion. Some experts felt that the people of Souther Fell had experienced an optical illusion, perhaps based on real troops who were exercising many miles away in Scotland. Could their images have somehow been reflected in the clouds to reappear upon a mountain top in Cumberland? If that had been the case, it did not explain the sightings in 1735 and 1737.

This, however, is not the only account of spectral armies. On the eve of the Battle of Marston Moor in Yorkshire (1644) the ghosts of a phantom army were seen on Helvellyn, and another ghostly army equipped with pikestaffs was seen on a hill in Leicestershire.

A similar account was witnessed on the Mendip Hills in Somerset while a remarkable event occurred on Christmas Eve, 1642, at Edgehill near Stratford-upon-Avon.

A group of local people, including shepherds and villagers, were celebrating Christmas between midnight and one o'clock in the morning, when they were suddenly surrounded by a ghostly party of Royalists. The soldiers were governed by Prince Rupert and there was also a party of Roundheads with whom the Royalists did battle. The local people could hear the sounds of the conflict, the groans of the injured and dying, the calls of the officers; they could see the battle colours of each side as the fight continued around them. But the actual Battle of Edgehill had occurred during the previous October. This was a repeat of that battle – by ghosts – and it was repeated in successive years in front of other witnesses.

In most of these cases, experts believe these are optical illusions, being refracted and magnified upon the clouds or vapours and that they are sightings of actual events which are occurring simultaneously many miles away. But that does not account for the repetition of the Battle of the Edgehill. And so the ghostly army of Souther Fell remains an intriguing mystery.

Blencathra features in another piece of lore. Lying in a deep hollow between this mountain and Souther Fell is a small tarn called Scales Tarn. It is so deep in the fells that local tradition says the sun never reaches the water.

One claim is that at noon, it is possible to see reflections of stars in the surface. One other legend is that this tarn is of enormous depth – some local people even say it is bottomless.

29   Thirlmere and Dunmail Raise

The Death of a King, a Bride and Mr Clark

Modern maps continue to show Dunmail Raise. It is a high point on the dual carriageway of the A591 as it sweeps through the Cumbrian mountains between Grasmere and Keswick via Thirlmere. It is some two-and-a-half miles north of Grasmere and until 1974 marked the county boundary which separated Cumberland from Westmorland. In that year, the two countries lost their identities to become the new county of Cumbria.

Nearby are Raise Beck, Raise Cottage and Raise Bridge, while beyond is the re-structured lake of Thirlmere. Dunmail Raise itself is marked by a large pile of rocks which is between the two lanes of the dual carriageway. Few passing travellers will appreciate the historic significance of this pile of stones, but it is the site of an important battle.

The pile of rocks is said to commemorate the final resting place of Dunmail, the last King of Cumberland. He was killed in AD 945, more than a thousand years ago. His death occurred as he fought the combined forces of Malcolm, the King of Scotland and Edmund, the Saxon king. Dunmail was killed by Edmund and as the Cumberland king lay dead, Edmund ordered his troops to make prisoners of Dunmail's men; having done this, they were then forced to carry hundreds of rocks and boulders and heap them upon the corpse of their leader.

Edmund believed that the resultant pile of stones would forever be a memorial to his victory, and Dunmail's lands were then handed over to Malcolm, King of Scotland. Dunmail's two sons, who had fought at his side, then had their eyes gouged out, while the golden crown of Dunmail was carried up the nearby hill and thrown into Grisedale Tarn. With that final gesture, the reign of the Cumberland kings was over.

There is very little to add to this tale except that Dunmail is probably not buried there at all, and that the present pile of stones is probably not the original! There is even doubt about whether Dunmail was a real person.

Theorists argue that the term 'dun' means nothing more than a heap of stone, although in Scotland it means a small fort built with stone walls. Of further interest is a custom which was popular years ago – when two armies met for conflict, every soldier from each side would place a stone on a pile. The victorious ones would then return to remove a stone. Other experts say that the word 'mail' also means a pile of stones, as does the word 'raise'.

In spite of such doubts, the legend of the burial of Dunmail at this point has long been a Lakeland folk story, but further doubts arise following the construction of Manchester's reservoir at Thirlmere. When teams of Irish labourers arrived to begin construction of the new reservoir, they were told the story of Dunmail Raise, which is only half a mile from the tip of the lake. Some of them grew to believe that the huge cairn concealed a buried treasure. After discussing the matter over a few drinks in a local inn, they decided to search for that treasure. Working with the gusto that only enthusiastic Irish labourers could muster, they demolished Dunmail's historic cairn. Unfortunately, they failed to find anything of value. Perhaps their joint conscience made them realize their folly and so they decided to rebuild the mighty cairn – and so they did, albeit adding many more rocks and stones of their own. In their view, they had rebuilt it so that it was in far better shape than before! Their well-intended actions, however, did not please everyone and so the authorities instructed them to return the cairn to its original size and shape.

Even so, the Irishmen were upset at the criticism and when they had re-shaped the pile of stones, they still added several more pieces in recompense for the damage they thought they had done. Thus the cairn on Dunmail Raise is probably nothing like the original constructed over a thousand years ago.

Not that it really would matter to King Dunmail – the truth seems to be that he is not buried there at all. Some time after the legendary battle of Dunmail Raise, he went on a pilgrimage to Rome and died there. He was, in all probability, buried in Rome.

Oddly enough, the story of the Irishmen seeking buried treasure does not feature a golden crown which was supposedly thrown into Grisedale Tarn. So far as I know, no serious attempt by anyone has been made to retrieve that very desirable treasure.

Thirlmere is beside the road beyond Dunmail Raise on the way to Keswick. This modest lake has had several names, including Leatheswater, Brackenwater, Brackmere, Layswater, Leeswater, Wyborn Water and Tirlmeer. Now largely concealed by conifers, many of which are foreign species, it was once a pretty Cumberland lake but towards the end of the last century, the valley was dammed and transformed into a reservoir. It was done to serve the people of Manchester which it continues to do, but it is not the only lake which provides water for Manchester – Haweswater is another (see Haweswater).

At Thirlmere, work began in August 1890 and it was completed in October, 1894 by which time the level of Thirlmere had risen by some fifty-four foot. This doubled the lake's capacity and flooded the valley. In doing so, it submerged several buildings including farms, cottages and an inn of the village of Wythburn, plus a large house known as Armboth House. In addition, it also submerged an unusual causeway known as the Celtic Bridge. In its original form, Thirlmere looked almost as if it was two lakes because there was a narrow channel which connected the two sections. This was crossed by a ford and the old causeway bridge.

All that has disappeared. One survivor was the tiny white-walled church at Wythburn; originally, it was also threatened by the rising water, but the reservoir's builders decided not to flood it. Although they did consider its demolition and subsequent rebuilding on higher ground! This never happened – the church was left in peace and the lake's rising water was never allowed to threaten it. The fact that Wordsworth loved the church, and that it was of such diminutive size, may have saved it from being lost forever beneath Thirlmere. The church, with a chancel added in 1872, stands close to the A591 on the shores of Thirlmere and is the only survivor of the former community of Wythburn. Its car park is now utilized by those who wish to climb Helvellyn but today, when the waters are low, the remains of the other old buildings can be seen.

With regard to Armboth House, it was claimed that this was the most haunted house in Cumberland. It stood at the foot of Armboth Fell which is midway along the western bank of Thirlmere and the story has entered the folklore of the Lake District. Some two centuries ago, the daughter of the family was about to be married at Hallowe'en (October 31) when a stranger rushed into the house. He shouted to the assembled guests that the bride had been pushed into the lake and drowned.

At the time, no one knew who had murdered the girl, although the bridegroom was suspected for a long time afterwards, but at every following Hallowe'en, there was a series of turbulent hauntings at Armboth House. Bells would ring in the middle of the night, furniture would move without human assistance, crockery would tumble to the floor, lights would suddenly appear and disappear, weird noises would occur and the wedding breakfast-table would be mysteriously relaid when everyone was asleep. Even the ghostly form of a large dog was seen swimming in the lake.

Eventually, stories of these ghosts reached such a pitch that it was said that every ghost in the Lake District came to join the festivities, including the Calgarth Skulls (see Windermere). Reports of those ghostly revels led the local people to believe that the spirit of the drowned bride was returning each year to sit at her wedding breakfast table.

These disturbing events led to suggestions of a poltergeist in the premises but no one is now able to investigate those claims because the house is under water.

Lake Thirlmere has also produced another folk tale. A large rock which juts into the lake is known as Clark's Loup. Loup is a local word meaning leap, and it was from this rock that a man called Clark leapt to his death by drowning. It seems that Mr Clark was of a very jealous disposition and this was not helped by the fact that his wife had lots of admirers whom she deliberately encouraged.

Her behaviour so upset her husband that he decided to commit suicide. But, being somewhat indecisive, Mr Clark could not decide which was the best method. He considered hanging himself from a beam of the house, but his wife told him that this was a most painful way of dying – and there was no guarantee he would succeed. He thought of shooting himself but his wife said he was the worst shot in the area and he might succeed only in causing a severe injury.

It seems that Mr Clark next considered drowning himself; he'd heard stories that it was just like drifting off to sleep and to this his wife agreed. She said it was a most pleasurable way of dying and offered to help him. And so they walked to Thirlmere where she took him on to the lofty rock and advised him to jump into the depths. He took off his outer clothes, made a long run towards the edge to clear the submerged stones beneath, and landed deep in the lake.

He sank into the water as Mrs Clark watched from the safety of the rock which now bears her family name. When she was satisfied he had died, she went home to continue her life while posterity records his death in the name of that rock.

In addition to Clark's Loup, there is another stone which is of interest. It is called the Rock of Names. One day, William Wordsworth, his sister Dorothy, his wife Mary and her sister Sarah Hutchinson, his brother John Wordsworth (who died at sea in 1805) and the poet Samuel Taylor Coleridge all came to a point near Black Crag for a picnic.

This was close to the old turnpike road which is now under Thirlmere's water. Upon John Wordsworth's insistence, each of them carved their initials on a rock. It took a long time but they persisted and so this unusual memorial stood by the roadside until the construction of Thirlmere Reservoir. It was decided by Manchester Corporation to save the Rock of Names from the flooding and present it to the citizens of Cockermouth, the market town which was Wordsworth's birthplace. But when the rock was lifted from its bed, it crumbled into small pieces. It was decided not to attempt the journey to Cockermouth and instead, the pieces were re-assembled into a form of cairn and placed beside the road on the Helvellyn side. It was some three hundred yards to the north of the straining well which is on the lakeside between Wythburn and Thirlspot. The well is shown on many maps.

By 1984, however, the Rock of Names was deteriorating to such an extent that it was removed for renovation. Its crumbling state meant it could not be moved as one piece and so it was demolished and re-assembled as a curious sculpture. It is now safe behind Dove Cottage at Grasmere, Wordsworth's former home and now the Wordsworth Museum.

30   Threlkeld

A Saint and a Skull

For such a small village, Threlkeld has a wealth of interest. It lies below the majesty of Saddleback (Blencathra), a long line of cottages in grey, red and white, and is some four miles east of Keswick along the A66 towards Penrith.

In prehistoric times, the mountain slopes were the site of an ancient civilization while the name of Threlkeld may come from Viking times. One theory is that it means Thrall's Well, Thrall being a landowner and keld being an old northern word for a well or spring.

The present parish church of St Mary was built in 1777 and underwent a major restoration in 1911. It has a curiously open appearance, devoid of the normal aisles and church interiors, and is rather like a large hall. Rather plainly built of grey rendered stone, it has a tiny tower but it contains two bells which are at least 500 years old and a black letter bible dating to 1613. The font is fashioned from Threlkeld granite, granite-quarrying being a local industry until 1980. We found the organ hidden behind a heavy curtain in one corner.

The church is the focus of a charming local custom. When a parishioner makes a promise to marry, he or she has to pay five shillings (25p) to church funds for distribution to the poor of the parish if he or she breaks that promise.

The village was well known for its support of rural sports. It was once renowned for its Cumberland wrestlers and later for being the home of many noted huntsmen. A monument in the churchyard commemorates forty-five of those huntsmen, one of whom is John Crozier. He was master of the local foxhounds for sixty-four years and died aged eighty. The Blencathra Fell pack of hounds, founded in 1840, is based in the village which is also known for its sheep dog trials.

Some distance out of the village is Threlkeld Hall but this is not the original. The original was the home of Sir Lancelot Threlkeld who boasted that he owned three great houses – one for pleasure, one for profit and warmth in the winter, and the third to provide tenants to accompany him to battle. Thelkeld Hall was the latter. The Hall is associated with a moving Yorkshire folk story (see Brougham). A pile of stones and the remains of a moat to the south of the present Hall are all that remains of Sir Lancelot's house.

Sir Lancelot married the widowed Lady Clifford whose son was in danger of being murdered by the Yorkists. The boy came to Threlkeld in secret and was reared as a shepherd on the Lakeland fells, only resuming his role as Lord Henry Clifford when it was safe to do so. He became known as the Shepherd Lord.

One of Threlkeld's own folk tales involves St Kentigern. In AD 555, he came here from Scotland and erected a cross before which he said mass and preached to the local people. Kentigern was not his only name, however. He was popularly known as Mungo, after which Mungris-dale, a short distance from Threlkeld, is named. Kentigern was a bishop who died around AD 612; his feast day is 14 January and he was a native of Lothian, Scotland. The story of his birth is one of romance and danger. His mother was Thenew, the daughter of a Welsh king and the object of lust by a local chieftain. When Thenew refused to marry him, her father expelled her from the house and made her work as a labourer in the fields. There, the lustful chieftain pursued and raped her after which she became pregnant. Being pregnant before marriage was a capital offence and the death sentence was pronounced; Thenew would be lashed to a chariot wheel and hurled from the top of a mountain. Miraculously, she survived that ordeal and so she was placed in a small boat and cast adrift on the sea.

Again by some miracle, she drifted north and was washed ashore in the Firth of Forth. There she gave birth to a baby boy and was found by a hermit who took her into his rough shelter and cared for her. The hermit, a religious man, named the child Kentigern which meant chief of the lord. The boy grew into a fine child, learning much from the wise old hermit who assumed the role of foster father.

Then, as a young man, Kentigern went to Glasgow where he followed his foster father into the priesthood. He established Christianity in Glasgow but when persecution drove him from Scotland, he decided to flee to Wales. He was recalled, however, by the Christian King Rederech and part of his work included the conversion of the Lake District.

So it was that he came to Threlkeld to erect his cross and preach to the people. While he was in Scotland, however, he is said to have worked a miracle – he saved an unfaithful wife from death after she had been attacked by her angry husband. A ring and a fish in the heraldic arms of the City of Glasgow are said to commemorate that event and he was later canonized a saint.

His nickname, Mungo, comes from Munghu, a Celtic word meaning 'most dear', a reflection on the charming personality of St Kentigern. As St Mungo, however, he has given his name to several places including Mungrisdale, Mungoswells and Mungasdale.

Threlkeld is also the location of a tale about a troublesome skull. It is similar to the Calgarth Skulls story (see Windermere) and the Brougham Skull (see Brougham).

Years ago, at a house called Threlkeld Place, a new tenant farmer discovered a skull. It was in a small, dark room which had not been used by the previous occupant, but the new tenant did the honourable thing and gave it a decent burial. But when his wife returned to the room, the skull had mysteriously and rapidly returned; it was resting on a niche in the wall.

This alarmed the farmer so much that he took the skull to the coast and threw it in the sea at St Bees Head but when he returned home, it had, yet again, mysteriously returned to its place in the niche. From that point, several very determined attempts were made to dispose of that skull, but in every case it mysteriously made its way back to the small room. Eventually, it was decided to conceal it within the wall and so it was bricked up.

We are not told whether any ghostly or unexplained noises or occurrences disturbed the household while the skull was in the open, but the tenant farmer and his wife quickly left to find work on another farm.

31   Ullswater

The Legend of Aira Force – and Some Cheese!

There are times when Lake Ullswater looks positively black and gloomy. An air of mystery hangs over the still waters and there is often a hint of intrigue in the air.

From a personal point of view, I enjoy this lake; it never fails to provide an air of calm, even in midwinter, and I like to wander around its shores or picnic upon its stony beaches. The surrounding hills are rich with tradition and I can recommend a drive through Howtown followed by a walk into the heights of Martindale. Alternatively, you can make your way from the shore via Dockray to explore the quieter villages upon the fells. Around this lake, you can experience the more remote majesty of England's Lakeland and at the same time look down upon its restful waters.

Ullswater, once known as Eusemere, is almost eight miles long and it stretches from Pooley Bridge near Penrith to Glenridding and Patterdale; the A592 runs along the western shore and provides some beautiful views of the lake from the shoreline while a network of narrow lanes offers the privilege of seeing Lakeland villages which have not been ruined by the invasion of tourists.

Even before Wordsworth's time, tourists were beginning to explore the Lake District but Dorothy favoured Ullswater because, in contrast with other parts of lakeland, it had not been adversely affected by large numbers of people. She and William came on

Thursday, 15 April 1802 and he took a walk which you can follow.

At a point where the road from Dockray joins the A592 near the lakeside at Gowbarrow, there is a convenient car park. By leaving the car here, you can climb a stile at the other side of the road and follow a path which goes to the shores of the lake. If you visit this quiet place in April, you might see some daffodils.

When William and Dorothy Wordsworth walked at this place they saw some daffodils and Dorothy made a note of the fact in her diary. She noticed a long belt of them along the shore and said that some rested their heads on the stones as if using them for pillows while the rest tossed and reeled and danced and seemed to laugh as the wind from the lake blew among them. Some two years later, William Wordsworth remembered those daffodils and wrote his famous verse about wandering as lonely as a cloud and seeing a host of golden daffodils beside the lake, beneath the trees, fluttering and dancing in the breeze. Thus it was that the daffodils of Ullswater inspired this renowned verse.

Another of Wordsworth's inspirations came from nearby. A small beck tumbles and falls past the heights of Gowbarrow. The stream begins its journey in Deepdale between Great Dodd and Hartside and flows past Dockray before heading for its steep drop towards Ullswater. It flows beneath the road and emerges on Aira Point, close to where Wordsworth saw the daffodils. The stream is Aira Beck and during its tumbling journey towards the lake, it forms a series of spectacular waterfalls. One of these is called High Force and another is known as Aira Force. A footpath runs nearby and close to the bottom is a feature known as Lyulph's Tower. This is not open to the public but was built by the Duke of Norfolk in 1780 as a hunting lodge.

Aira Force is the setting for one of the Lake District's best known folk tales, a romantic ballad with a very sad finale. Several writers have been inspired to produce stories and verses about this place and its associated legend. Wordsworth, for example, featured the waterfall in his poem called 'Airey Force Valley' written in 1836, he also wrote a poem called 'The Somnambulist' which was inspired by this tale and Thomas de Quincy also made use of it in his work 'An apparition at Airey Force'. We now call the falls Aira (not Airey) Force. Force or foss is a northern word for waterfall, and there is a fine walk to the cataracts from the car park near Aira Point to which I referred earlier.

The story concerns events which happened a thousand years ago or even more. At that time, there was a castle on the hills above the waterfall, some slight distance north of where Lyulph's Tower now stands. A mighty lord lived in the castle and he had a beautiful daughter called Lady Emma. Brave and gallant knights came from far and wide in their efforts to woo this lovely maiden. They brought precious gifts for her and regaled her with stories of their daring, but she rejected every one of them. There was only one man for Emma – and he was the bold Sir Eglamore.

Eglamore was renowned throughout the country for his strength and bravery; he was a famous warrior who fought with enormous success in many battles but his fame meant that he was seldom at home. He spent many long months overseas, fighting in the Middle East and conquering those who would bring evil to the world. Emma missed him greatly, but not once did she complain and never did she betray him. Her love was total, her loyalty was complete.

Eglamore did return home from time to time and the happy couple spent hours walking in the woods near Aira Force, but the more successful that Eglamore became, the longer were his absences. And, the longer his absences, the more she missed him.

Lady Emma eventually reached the stage where she could not sleep at night through longing for her beloved. She became restless and soon began to walk in her sleep.

In this dreamlike state, she would walk to the edge of the waterfall, renewing in her mind the happy times she had spent with Eglamore. And then, her dreams fulfilled, she would return to her bed and sleep until morning. But events were to take a most dramatic and terrible turn.

Late one night when the falls were heavy with fresh water, Lady Emma began to walk in her sleep and, as on previous occasions, wandering in a trance towards the roaring waterfall at Aira. She arrived and stood on top of the precipice above the noisy foaming water, the roaring of the tumbling cascade preventing her from hearing any other sound.

Unknown to Emma, the bold Sir Eglamore was on his way home from battle and was urging his tired horse to its greatest effort as he approached the castle of Lady Emma. His final mile took him along the footpath which borders the waterfall, but Emma never heard his approach due to the continuous sound of the crashing water.

As Eglamore entered the clearing above the falls, he was astonished to see the figure of Lady Emma standing in the moonlight. She was on the edge of the cliff, clad only in her flimsy night attire and she seemed to be in a trance; he gazed upon her from a distance, not knowing whether he was seeing a spirit of some kind, or whether this was indeed his true Lady Emma. Quietly, and not wishing to disturb the illusion, he dismounted and walked quietly towards her.

She was standing on rocks at the very edge of the cataract, peering with unseeing eyes into the chasm below and the more that Eglamore watched, the more uncertain he was. Could this be Emma? If it was, why had she not responded to his presence? She was behaving as if she was bewitched, as if she was a phantom rather than a real person.

After a few moments, Eglamore decided to touch the figure. Gently, he reached out and touched her bare arm. The shock awoke her immediately but she was so terrified to find herself at the edge of the waterfall that she shrieked in abject fear, lost her footing in her anxiety to get away from the edge, and slipped into the chasm. Her fragile body was carried down by the fierce torrent of floodwater and in seconds she was being swept to her death. Her frail body was battered against the rocks, her face was submerged and her struggles were useless against the terrible power of that water.

Sir Eglamore, the most gallant of warriors, made a supreme effort to save her. He leapt into the raging torrent, risking his own life in his desire to save Lady

Emma. Through determination, bravery and perhaps little good fortune, he managed to reach her. She had been battered by the rocks and submerged beneath the raging flood, and she was still unconscious as he carried her to safety.

He laid her on the side of the stream and she recovered consciousness for the briefest of moments, only long enough to realize that Eglamore was at her side. She took his hands in hers and, weakened by her terrible experience, asked him to take her in his arms. Tenderly, he did so; he kissed her with tears rolling down his cheeks and in those precious last moments, Emma died.

Eglamore was heartbroken. Devastated, he laid her on the bare earth and knelt at her side for a long, long time before carrying her back home to inform her father and her family.

He blamed himself for causing her death. He felt his actions had caused her to fall into the chasm of roaring flood waters and so he retired from his war-like activities. He became a monk and built a cell above Aira Force where he spent the rest of his life as a hermit, always in deep prayer. He also built a small bridge across the chasm so that others might never be at risk from the powerful waters. But Sir Eglamore never did overcome his grief at the loss of Lady Emma.

This oft-repeated yarn has led to reports of ghostly ladies being seen near Aira Force and upon one occasion, a local woman gave an account of how she became trapped by the wet, steep rocks, having somehow walked into what she described, via the pen of De Quincey, as 'a semi-circus, all lofty, all perpendicular, all glazed with trickling water or smooth as polished porphyry ... She started to panic and wondered if she would ever succeed in climbing out of the hole when a ghostly woman appeared. She was dressed in white muslin and beckoned for our intrepid explorer to follow her to safety. As the explorer drew closer to an exit route she had never seen before, she realized that the apparition was in fact her own sister – later, she was to find that her sister had never left the house.

Another lovely folk tale comes from Matterdale, a tiny

place about a mile and a half from the shores of Ullswater along the A5091 to Keswick and Penrith. This is just one of many stories about the tough cheese of Lakeland. In this case, a farmer from Patterdale was on his way to Keswick Fair with a cart load of his home-made cheeses. They were so heavy that when he was climbing towards Matterdale End, the cart collapsed and the cheeses fell into the highway; they began to roll down the valley towards Ullswater, moving off the road to bump and bounce across the fells. As they rolled from rock to rock, their tough skins acted like flints and caused sparks which set the surrounding moorland alight. The fire burnt for three weeks afterwards!

Among the stories of tough cheeses are those which say that some Lakelanders sharpened their knives on them, others used them for soling their boots or clogs and some used them instead of flints for lighting domestic fires. Most Cumberland cheeses had skins so tough that no knife would cut them while the contents were such that they provided exercise for the teeth rather than nourishment for the body!

The most extraordinary tale comes from 1866 when a soldier of the 3rd Royal Lancashire Regiment stole a piece of cheese from the Moorcock, an inn near Sedbergh. The skin was so hard that for four years on active service, he used it as a flint for his flintlock rifle!

32 Watendlath

Endless Bliss

The chief problem with Watendlath, so far as visitors are concerned, is how to pronounce its name. It comprises three syllables – What-end-lath – with some emphasis upon the middle one and there is a charming tale which assists in the correct pronunciation.

Before I repeat the story, I will say that every visitor to the Lake District should make the journey to Watendlath. It is a tiny village consisting of three farmsteads and thanks to the National Trust, which owns the farms, the village is totally unspoilt. One of the farms does offer refreshments, however, but it is truly a delightful place.

The only access by road is from the lakeside of Derwent Water. One must leave the B5289 about two miles south of Keswick and drive a further two miles along a very narrow but very picturesque road. It runs through spectacular scenery and crosses Lakeland's prettiest bridge *en route*. This is Ashness Bridge where a pause will provide a classic view of Derwent Water with Skiddaw in the distance. Further towards Watendlath there is Surprise View. Looking from the top of a crag at this roadside point, one can see the lake, the mountains and their environs in a dramatic and panoramic aspect.

The tiny community of Watendlath is beside Watendlath Tarn, fed by several streams which descend the surrounding fells. It is the spectacular flow from this small lake which itself tumbles down the fells to become Lodore Falls. There is a pretty single-arch bridge over the beck at Watendlath, and after leaving the tarn near the village, the water crashes over rocks in a narrow gap known as The Churn. One can picnic around the tarn or climb the nearby fells; here, it is possible to find peace away from the honeypots of the more densely populated Lakeland.

Watendlath features in the *Rogue Herris* series of novels by Sir Hugh Walpole (1884–1941). He lived in Borrowdale and set his stories in that area; one of the novels, *Judith Paris*, uses Watendlath as its background and so successful were these books that some readers thought Judith Paris was a real person. They came to believe that she really did live in a farmhouse in Watendlath, and that myth is perpetuated today. When I called at the village, I had refreshments in the very farm house that the character of Judith Paris inhabited. In such circumstances, it is difficult to believe she was not a real person.

There is, however, a pleasing tale which tells us how to correctly pronounce Watendlath. It concerns a young couple who got married a long, long time ago. The husband, a lover of the Lake District, brought his bride to Watendlath which then had another name, not now recorded. They stayed in one of the farm houses, walking around the tarn, spending blissful moments exploring the hills and generally enjoying the calm and peaceful atmosphere.

The young woman, however, had a lisp and it is said that, soon after their arrival, she fell hopelessly in love with the village. As she walked around the tarn on the arm of her husband, she lisped, 'What endleth blith to live forever in a plathe like thith!' Ever since, the village has been called Watendlath and so we all know how to pronounce the name.

33 Windermere

The Skulls of Calgarth

Windermere is England's largest lake and it is some
ten-and-a-half miles long by a mile-and-a-half broad at its
widest point. Shaped rather like a dog's hind leg, it runs
almost north to south and is the most commercialized of
the English lakes. Boating, water-skiing, swimming and
other water sports are practised here while the centres of
population, Windermere, Ambleside and Bowness are
always busy with visitors, holidaymakers and climbers.
There are fine hotels, pleasing cafés and restaurants,
campsites and self-catering accommodation with a rich
variety of places to visit. Even so, there are quiet corners
and an excursion into the hills above the lake will reveal
some stunning landscapes and extraordinary views.

Windermere village owes its name to the railway. The
main line was planned from London to Carlisle, with a
branch line through Oxenholme, Kendal and Ambleside,
possible continuing to Keswick via a tunnel. During its
construction in 1847, it was decided not to extend it any
further than the village of Birthwaite, some distance short
of Ambleside and a long way short of Keswick. Birthwaite
overlooked Lake Windermere, but the terrain made it too
difficult and too expensive to progress to Keswick as
planned.

Because travellers might not recognize Birthwaite as the
station for Lake Windermere, it was decided to name the
station Windermere. The popularity of the line led to a
vast influx of visitors (whom Wordsworth had warned
against in 1844 by writing, 'Is there no nook of English

ground secure from rash assault?) and this in turn led to the establishment of hotels and guest-houses, plus the building of new homes and business premises. Soon, the village of Birthwaite was lost among the buildings of the new Windermere; this, in turn, has expanded to merge with nearby Bowness-on-Windermere to produce one large conurbation. Bowness is much older than Windermere; its church dates to 1483 and was itself the replacement of an earlier one destroyed by fire but the two centres are now virtually one town.

Windermere, therefore, is not an historic place but it is a busy and thriving tourist centre which has the fortune to be located in a stunningly beautiful situation. And the railway continues to bring passengers to Birthwaite in its modern guise as Windermere.

One interesting village near the lake is Sawry; there are, in fact two Sawrys, Far Sawry and Near Sawry, the latter being the home of children's author Beatrix Potter whose former house, Hill Top, is open to the public. Far Sawry is about one mile away from the lakeside through a steep and twisting lane from the Windermere ferry landing and this is the focus of one curious folk tale.

From the Sawry side of the lake, a narrow piece of land juts into the lake and upon this stands Ferry House, a large stone building with the appearance of an hotel. It is in fact the offices of The Institute of Freshwater Ecology and the Freshwater Biological Association. It is from this point that the modern car ferry sails; it carries up to eighteen cars at twenty-minute intervals and deposits them at the other side of the lake at a point called The Nab. This is another jutting piece of land, and the distance across the water is only quarter of a mile.

In times past, the ferry was a mere rowing boat which carried a handful of passengers. People who wished to cross the lake had to shout for the ferryman. If he was at one side of the lake, he could hear the shout of 'ferry' from the other bank and he would respond. But after an incident in the sixteenth century, it was a long time before any ferryman would respond to such a call.

The reason was a fearsome spectre known as the Crier of Claife. The crier occupied the tree-covered hills above

Sawry, these being known as Claife Heights and it lured unsuspecting people to their deaths. The best-known of these stories occurred some 400 years ago. On a very stormy night some travellers were in the ferry house along with the ferryman, and it seems they were having a merry time. As they laughed and drank, they heard a shout from The Nab at the other side of the lake. It was the familiar call for the ferry.

The ferryman, a quiet, unassuming man, responded to the request in spite of the adverse weather conditions. Off he went to honour his commitment. He disappeared into the darkness intended to row across to The Nab to collect his waiting passenger. But he did not return within the expected time.

The worried gathering of friends and travellers went down to the shore to seek him. In the darkness, they could hear neither the sound of his rowing nor his merry chatter with a passenger. As the search party approached the shoreline, the waiting party grew increasingly concerned. By this time, the ferryman was long overdue.

When they reached the edge of the lake, however, they found him. His ferry had been beached and he was alone, a wreck of a man. He was speechless with fear and had the appearance of someone who had endured a terrible ordeal. Such was his fear that he could not speak; he was unable to say what had happened to him and so he was put to bed, but by the next morning he was in a terrible state of fever.

The ferryman never recovered from his awful experience and died within a few days. He never did tell anyone what had happened but everyone knew it was the work of something very evil – and everyone knew the awful reputation of the Crier of Claife. For months afterwards, weird cries could be heard at The Nab, especially when the weather was stormy, but if these were genuine calls for the ferry, no ferryman ever responded. They believed that a ghostly spectre was calling for the ferry to lure unsuspecting ferrymen to their deaths. The fate of their colleague had been enough to persuade the ferrymen of Windermere never to respond to such calls. This terrible spectre could be none other than the evil Crier of Claife.

Clearly, the fear generated by these tales had a detrimental effect upon the business of the ferry and eventually, it was decided to make an attempt to rid the lake of the crier. The services of a priest were necessary.

The local people called upon a monk from Furness Abbey who, at that time, was living as a hermit on one of the islands in Windermere. After being told of the fate of the ferryman, he said he would exorcize the spirit of the Crier of Claife. On Christmas Day, he assembled his congregation and during mass in their presence, said the spirit of the Crier of Claife would be removed from the lake and confined to a remote quarry in the woods on Claife Heights. The people then accompanied the priest to the quarry for the final part of the exorcism ceremony and, according to old records, the crier was laid there at that service. It appears to have been a successful attempt because the call of the Crier of Claife was never heard again but it was a long time before normal ferry services were resumed.

Even so, no one went to that quarry at night and it was said that if foxhounds chased a fox into the area, they would stop as they approached the quarry. Some unknown fear deterred them from going any further. A later story told of a schoolmaster who went to examine the legend of the crier by visiting the quarry, but he was never seen again. Not surprisingly, the quarry became known as Crier Quarry and the surrounding woods became known as Crier Woods.

Windermere boasts another curious folk tale with ghostly connotations. Just north of Windermere village, close to the point where the Trout Beck enters the lake, there is an area known as Calgarth Park. In the grounds years ago stood an old house called Calgarth Hall and it produced one of the most enduring folk stories of the Lake District. The tale is known as the Skulls of Calgarth. There are similar tales of Threlkeld (see Threlkeld) and Brougham (see Brougham).

The Calgarth Skulls could not be destroyed in spite of a series of attempts to dispose of them. They had been buried on the fells, hidden in the countryside, thrown into the lake and even smothered in lime but on every occasion, they returned to haunt the occupiers of Calgarth Hall.

The story behind this curious haunting involved a man called Myles Philipson who was a justice of the peace. He was not an honest or pleasant man and he began to covet some land and premises owned by an elderly couple. They were Kraster and Dorothy Cook. When Philipson made an offer to buy their property, they rejected it and made it clear that they had no intention to sell it.

The greedy and determined Philipson then began a devious scheme to secure the property. He started by inviting Kraster and Dorothy to his house for a Christmas dinner. When they left, he accused them of stealing a silver cup from his house and called upon the constable to make a search of their home. The missing cup was found in circumstances which made it appear that the Cooks had indeed stolen it. As burglary was a capital offence, it meant that if they were found guilty, the Cooks would suffer the death penalty and their property would be forfeited. It would then become available for purchase by Philipson.

The Cooks were tried, found guilty and hanged at Appleby. In the minds of those who knew them, they were totally innocent of any such crime, the entire plot being hatched by Myles Philipson in his determination to secure their land and house. The crooked skills of Philipson, his planting of the evidence and his manipulation of the court proceedings resulted in the execution of Mr and Mrs Cook. It was a dreadful miscarriage of justice.

Before she died, however, Dorothy Cook laid a curse on Calgarth Hall and all who would benefit from it. She said it would become the most expensive ground a Philipson would ever purchase; she said no Philipson would ever prosper, nor would any of their offspring. She went on to say that while Calgarth's walls stood, she and her husband would haunt it day and night.

It was a short time afterwards that two skulls appeared at Calgarth Hall. No one knew where they had come from but vigorous attempts were made to get rid of them. They were thrown in the lake, buried on the fells, powdered and thrown to the winds and given all manner of terrible treatments.

But in spite of everything, they always returned to Calgarth Hall. When further unsuccessful attempts were made to get rid of the skulls, it was decided to build them into the walls of the Hall. The Philipsons of the time did so, but the family never did prosper nor could it produce any heirs.

The old Hall fell into disrepair and a new one was constructed close to the site. Likewise, the old house owned by the Cooks was also demolished and a new one built on its site. The modern Calgarth Hall does not incorporate the two skulls and so their present whereabouts are unknown.

As always in a story of this kind, attempts have been made to determine the truth. In the seventeenth century there was a local family called Philipson, of whom Christopher was a justice of the peace. He died in 1634. There was also a Myles Philipson who lived at Crook in the seventeenth century. Crook is between Bowness-on-Windermere and Kendal; Crook Hall used to be the home of the Philipsons and one of them, Robert, was known locally as Robin the Devil because of his adventures. He was a Royalist officer and on one occasion was besieged by Cromwell's troops on Belle Isle, on Windermere.

One writer called Clarke went so far as to accuse Robin the Devil as the killer of the innocent Mr and Mrs Cook while others believe that his Royalist sympathies may have made him the target of Cromwell; in other words, the tale of the murder was spread in order to discredit him.

The Philipsons were an historic local family, but none of them ever owned or occupied Calgarth Hall. It is odd that, after 1634, although the Philipsons acquired many estates and lots of land, they did suffer a range of mishaps, their estates became impoverished and the family went into a terminal decline.

About a century ago, the old Calgarth Hall was in a tumbledown condition. Originally built in the style of Levens Hall or Sizergh, it was once an elegant and splendid mansion but by the 1890s, it was occupied by working farmers who neglected it. But even at that time, the two skulls sat on a window ledge in one of the rooms and there were reports of hauntings and strange occurrences. It is claimed that one reason for the presence of the skulls was that the house had been owned by a lady doctor. She kept two human skeletons for use in connection with her work, and when the rest of the bones became lost or broken, she managed to retain the pair of skulls. These sat on a window ledge in Calgarth Hall for many years and might have been the source of this curious story.

Another tale says the house was eventually bought by a clergyman called Bishop Watson who exorcized the skulls and had them bricked up in one of the walls. He died in 1816 – he seems to have been a man of great imagination because one of his bizarre plans was to drain Lake Windermere to improve the land he owned!

But whatever the truth behind the tale of the Calgarth Skulls, and wherever they are now, it will live for many more years as a Lakeland folk story. A similar tale of a troublesome walled-up skull is located at Burton Agnes Hall near Bridlington in East Yorkshire.

Before leaving Windermere, reference should be made to the peculiar crop of inscribed rocks. They are beside the lake near Low Wood Inn which is between Ambleside and Windermere, and they bear a range of strange inscriptions which have no common theme. The best known is perhaps that which says '1833 – MONEY. LIBERTY. WEALTH. PEACE' while another says, 'A SLAVE LANDING ON THE BRITISH STRAND BECOMES FREE.' Some surfaces bear nothing but names.

Those names include Admiral Nelson, Captain Cook and other famous figures such as Dryden, Watt, Milton, Burns and Garrick. 'THE LIBERTY OF THE PRESS' is one carving, while another says, 'NATIONAL DEBT – £800,000,000'.

These inscribed rocks have become almost legendary in their own right, but they are the work of a mentally-ill man called John Longmire. He spent more than six years engraving them, working day and night in all weathers. Whilst no one knows why he embarked on this course, he has left behind something which is durable, intriguing and part of the Lake District's vast store of folk lore.